Make a Midrash Out of Me

Volume 1: From Chaos to Egypt

Joel Lurie Grishaver

Illustrated by George Shewchuk

Torah Aura Productions

ISBN 1-891662-51-1

Copyright © 2004 Torah Aura Productions

Artwork Copyright © 2004 George Shewchuk.

TORAH AURA PRODUCTIONS • 4423 FRUITLAND AVENUE, LOS ANGELES, CA 90058
(800) BE-TORAH • (800) 238-6724 • (323) 585-7312 • FAX (323) 585-0327
E-MAIL <MISRAD@TORAHAURA.COM> • VISIT THE TORAH AURA WEBSITE AT WWW.TORAHAURA.COM
PRINTED IN CANADA

Table of Contents

3

Make a Midrash Out of Me

Imagine looking at a photographic album with an older relative. You look at the photographic album and you see faces, old clothes, familiar and strange places. They look at the photographs and they see stories and memories. As you look at the photographs they tell you about the people and the moments. Uncle Charles who you see in the upper left hand corner used to play the horses. Aunt Amelia who is standing next to him used to make the best bundt cake. When this picture was taken it looks like I was smiling but actually my brother was pinching me behind my back.

The Torah is like the photographic album. It is the basic picture. Midrash is like the stories and the memories told to us by our relatives. They deepen and expand the stories in the Torah. They often give us memories that start with the Torah and go other places. They offer a rich tapestry of understanding.

Rashi is a famous Biblical commentator, Rabbi Shlomo Yitzḥaki. He lived in France in the 11th Century. He begins he commentary on the Torah by quoting his father. He says, "This text demands midrash." In essence he says that the Torah is saying, "Make a Midrash out of me." This book is created in that tradition. In is a invitation to create midrash in response to the Torah's call.

Make a Midrash Out of Me offers you the chance to study Torah, create your own midrashic responses, and study some famous traditional midrashim. Enjoy.

Joel Lurie Grishaver
5 Tammuz, 5764

4

Text 1

The Song of Creation

Genesis 1.1–2.4

1.

Narrator 1: [1.1]Beginnings: God created the sky and the land. [2]The land was unformed and chaotic. Darkness was over the face of the deep. The breath of God floated over the face of the waters. [3]And God said:

God: Let there be light.

Narrator 1: And there was light. [4]God saw that the light was:

God: Good.

Narrator 2: And God divided between the light and between the darkness. [5]God called the light:

God: Day.

Narrator 1: God called the darkness:

God: Night.

Chorus: There was evening. There was morning.

Narrator 2: Day One.

2.

Narrator 1: [6]God said:

God: Let there be a space inside the waters, and let it divide between waters under the space and waters over the space.

Narrator 1: ⁷And God made the space, and divided between the waters that were under the space and between the waters that were over the space. And it was so. ⁸God called the space:

God: Sky.

Chorus: There was evening. There was morning.

Narrator 2: A second day.

3.

Narrator 1: ⁹And God said:

God: Let the waters under the sky be gathered into one place so that dryness can be seen.

Narrator 2: ¹⁰And it was so. God called the dryness:

God: Land.

Narrator 2: God called the gathering of waters:

God: Seas.

Narrator 2: God saw that it was:

God: Good.

Narrator 1: ¹¹God said:

God: Let the land carpet itself with grass, seed-yielding vegetation and fruit trees.

Narrator 2: And it was so. ¹²And the land sprouted grasses, seed-yielding vegetation and fruit trees. God saw that it was:

God: Good.

Chorus: ¹³There was evening. There was morning.

Narrator 2: A third day.

4.

Narrator 1: ¹⁴God said:

God: Let there be lights in the space of the sky to divide between the day and between the night. They will be signs for the seasons, for the days and for the years. ¹⁵And they will be lights in the space of the sky to light the land.

Narrator 2: And it was so. [16]God made two great lights. The great light to rule the day. The small light to rule the night—and the stars, too. [17]God put them in the space of the sky [18]to light the earth, to rule in the day and in the night, and to divide between light and darkness. And God saw that it was:

God: Good.

Chorus: [19]There was evening. There was morning.

Narrator 2: A fourth day.

5.

Narrator 1: [20]God said:

God: Let the waters be filled with swarming spirits of life. And let the sky flutter with flying birds over the land and in the face of the space of the sky.

Narrator 2: [21]And God created the great sea serpents, and every spirit of life which crawls, and which swarms in the waters. And the flying birds, too. And God saw that it was:

God: Good.

Narrator 2: [22]God blessed them, saying:

God: Grow fruitful and become many and fill the waters in the sea and let there be many birds in the earth.

Chorus: [23]There was morning. There was evening.

Narrator 2: A fifth day.

6.

Narrator 1: [24]And God said:

God: Let the land put forth the spirit of life in beasts and crawling things and land life.

Narrator 2: And it was so. [25]God made the land life, all beasts and all that crawls on the earth. God saw that it was:

God: Good.

Narrator 1: [26]God said:

THE CANAANITE GAZETTE

Imagine that you are a reporter for the *Canaanite Gazette*. Conduct one of the following interviews.

1. Ask God: "Explain the order in which You created things."

2. Ask an animal (your choice of animal): "How did you feel about people being added to creation? Was creation better before or after people?"

3. Ask an angel: "God is all-powerful. God can do everything and anything. God doesn't get tired. Why then, did God *have* to rest on the seventh day?"

God: Let Us make people in Our image, in Our likeness. Let them rule over the fish of the sea and the birds of the sky, over the beasts, and all the land, and all that crawls on that land.

Narrator 2: [27] God created people in God's image. In God's image, God created people as male and female. [28] God blessed them. God said to them:

God: Be fruitful and become many and fill the earth, and master it. Rule over the fish of the sea, and the birds of the sky, and all life that crawls on the earth.

Narrator 2: [29] God said:

God: *Hinnei:* I give you all seed-yielding vegetation upon the face of the land, and every tree which is on it. Fruit of the trees: All of it shall be for you to eat, [30] and for all the land animals, and all the birds of the sky, and everything that crawls on earth which has in it the life force.

Narrator 2: And it was so. [31] God saw everything God had made. It was:

God: Very Good.

Chorus: There was evening. There was morning.

Narrator 2: The sixth day.

7.

Narrator 1: [2.1] The sky and the land were finished. [2] God finished all the work on the seventh day. On the seventh day God rested from all the work. [3] God blessed the seventh day and made it holy, because on it God rested from all the work. Everything had been created.

Narrator 2: [4] This is the family history of the skies and the earth.

Creating People: Midrash 1

Genesis Rabbah 8.4

Narrator:	Rabbi Berekiah said:
Rabbi Berekiah:	When the Holy One decided to create people, God saw that both righteous and wicked people would descend from them. God said:
God:	If I create people, wicked people will come from them; but if I do not create them, then righteous people will never be born.
Rabbi Berekiah:	What did the Eternal do?
	God hid from sight the wickedness that would be done in the future, focused on the good that would be done, and enlarged the size of God's mercy. Then God created people.
	We learn this from Psalms 1.6:
Torah:	For the Eternal sees the ways of the righteous, but the ways of the wicked shall be wiped out.
Rabbi Berekiah:	What does this mean?
	It means that God wiped out the ways of the wicked from sight and boosted the quality of mercy. Then God created people...

Creating People: Midrash 2

Genesis Rabbah 8.5

Narrator:	Rabbi Shimon said:
Rabbi Shimon:	When the Holy One started to create people, the angels divided into groups. Some of the groups said:
Some Angels:	Let people be created.
Rabbi Shimon:	While others urged:
Other Angels:	Do not create people.
Rabbi Shimon:	We learn this from Psalms 85.11:
Torah:	Love and truth fought together. Righteousness and peace went to war with each other
Rabbi Shimon:	Love said:

Love: Let them be created because they will perform acts of love.

Rabbi Shimon: Truth said:

Truth: Let them not be created because they are filled with lies.

Rabbi Shimon: Righteousness said:

Righteousness: Let them be created because they will do righteous deeds.

Rabbi Shimon: Peace said:

Peace: Let them not be created because they are full of violence.

Rabbi Shimon: What did the Eternal do?

God took truth and threw it to the ground. The angels came before the Holy One and said,

Ministering Angels: Ruler of the Cosmos! Truth is Your seal. Why do you hate it? Let truth spring up from the earth!

Rabbi Shimon: That is why it is written in the next verse (Psalms 85.12):

Torah: Let truth spring up from the earth.

Rabbi Huna: While the angels were arguing with each other, the Holy One, created people. God said to the angels

Narrator: Rabbi Huna the Elder, of Sepphoris said:

God: Cool it. People have already been made!

Questions

1. What is the lesson taught from each of these midrashim?

Midrash 1: _____

Midrash 2: _____

2. Why did God wipe out the ways of the wicked from sight and boost the quality of mercy?

_____

3. According to the second midrash, what is the meaning of "Let truth spring up from the earth?"

_____

My Creation of People Midrash

Write your own story of the moment when people were created.

_____

_____

_____

_____

_____

_____

_____

_____

_____

_____

_____

_____

_____

_____

_____

_____

_____

The Garden

Part I: The Garden Grows

Narrator 1: 2.4This is the family-history of the skies and the land and their creation from the day that Adonai, the God, made land and skies. 5There were not yet plants of the field in the land, there were not yet grasses of the field growing—because Adonai, the God, had not yet caused it to rain on the land—and because there was no Earthling to work the earth. 6A mist went up from the ground and gave drink to the whole face of the earth.

Narrator 2: 7Adonai, the God, formed the Earthling from the dust of the earth and breathed into his nose the soul of life. The Earthling had a living spirit.

Narrator 1: 8Adonai, the God, planted a Garden in Eden and put there the Earthling who had been shaped. 9Adonai, the God, made trees grow from the earth, every kind of tree which is nice to look at and good to eat.

The Tree of Life was in the middle of the Garden and the Tree of the Knowledge of Good From Evil... [15] Adonai, the God, took the Earthling and put him in the Garden of Eden, to work it and to keep it. [16]Then God, commanded the Earthling:

God: You may eat from every other tree in the garden except from the Tree of [17]the Knowledge of Good From Evil. You may not eat from it. On the day you eat from it, your death will come.

Narrator 2: [18]Adonai, the God, said:

God: It is not good that the Earthling is alone. I will make a companion who fits with the Earthling.

Narrator 1: [19]So Adonai, the God, formed from the soil all the wild beasts and all the birds. And brought each to the Earthling to see what the Earthling would call it. [20]Whatever the Earthling called the animal, that became its name... But for the Earthling, no helper who fit could be found.

Narrator 2: [21]Adonai, the God, made the Earthling sleep a deep sleep and took one rib and then closed in the flesh. [22]Adonai, the God, built the rib into a woman, and brought her to the Earthling.

Narrator 1: [23]The Earthling said:

Adam: This is the one, Bone from my bone, Flesh from my flesh. She shall be called WO—MAN because she was taken from MAN.

Narrator 2: [24]So a man will leave his father and his mother, he will cling to his wife, and they will become one flesh. [25]Now the two of them, the Earthling and his wife, were naked, but they were not embarrassed.

Part II: The Garden Divides and Reproduces

Narrator 1: [3]The snake was the sneakiest of the animals which Adonai, the God, had made. It said to the woman:

Snake: Did God really say that you may not eat from any of the trees in the Garden?

Narrator 2: [2]The woman said to the snake:

Woman: We may eat the fruit from any of the other trees in the garden, [3]but God said: "The fruit from the tree in the middle of the garden, you may not eat, and you may not touch it, or you will die."

Narrator 1: [4]The snake said to the woman:

13

Snake: You are not going to die. [5]Rather, God knows that on the day you eat from it, your eyes will be opened and you will be like gods, knowing "good" from "evil."

Narrator 2: [6]The woman saw that the tree was good for eating. That it was nice to look at and that the tree was a source of knowledge. She took a fruit and ate it. She gave it to her husband and he ate it.

Narrator 1: [7]The eyes of the two of them were opened, and they knew that they were naked. They sewed together fig leaves and made themselves clothing.

Narrator 2: [8]They heard the sound of Adonai, the God, walking around in the garden at the windy time of the day. The Earthling and his wife hid themselves from Adonai, the God, in the middle of the trees of the Garden.

Narrator 1: [9]Adonai, the God, called to the Earthling and said to him:

God: Where are you?

Narrator 1: [10]He said:

Adam: I heard you in the garden and I was afraid because I was naked, so I hid.

Narrator 2: [11]God said:

God: Who told you that you were naked? Did you eat from the tree that I commanded you not to eat from?

Narrator 1: [12]The Earthling said:

Adam: The woman whom you gave me to stand with me gave me from the tree and I ate.

Narrator 2: [13]God said to the woman:

God: What have you done?

Narrator 1: She said:

Woman: The serpent seduced me and I ate.

Narrator 2: [14]God said to the serpent:

God: Because you have done this, you are cursed among all beasts and from all living things. You will walk on your stomach. You will eat dust all the days of your life. [15]I will make you and the woman into enemies—your future-family will be enemies with her future-family. They will beat your head and you will bite their heels.

14

Narrator 1: ¹⁶To the woman God said:

God: I will majorly increase the pain you feel. With pain you will give birth to children. Your man's closeness you shall seek, but he shall rule over you.

Narrator 2: ¹⁷And God said to the Earthling:

God: Because you listened to your woman and ate from the tree from which I commanded you not eat, the earth will be cursed. With hard work you shall eat from it all the days of your life. ¹⁸Thorns and thistles shall grow from the earth. ¹⁹With the sweat of your brow you shall get bread to eat until you return to the earth from which you were taken. For you are dust and to dust you will return.

Narrator 1: ²⁰Then the Earthling called his woman by the name

Adam: Eve,

Narrator 1: which means "the giver of life", because she was going to be the mother of all the living.

Narrator 2: ²¹Adonai made Adam and Eve clothing and dressed them. ²²Adonai, the God, said:

God: Now people have become like Us, knowing Good from Evil. Next, they could take and eat from the Tree Of Life and live forever.

Narrator 2: ²³So Adonai, the God, banished them from the Garden of Eden to work the earth from which they were taken. ²⁴After they were driven out God settled them to the east of Eden. God placed a flaming ever-turning sword to guard the path to the Tree of Life.

THE CANAANITE GAZETTE

Imagine that you are a reporter for the *Canaanite Gazette*. Conduct the following interviews.

1. Ask the Snake: "What did you want with Eve? Why did you mess with her head?"

2. Ask Adam: "Where were you while the snake was fooling with your wife?"

3. Ask Eve: "God punished you with bearing children in pain, and Adam, your husband, renamed you 'Eve' (meaning the 'lifegiver'). How did that make you feel? What does that name mean to you?"

4. Ask God, Adam, Eve, and the Snake: "How do you feel about the way this story turned out? What do you think will happen in the future?"

Genesis Rabbah, 17.4

Torah: So Adonai, the God, formed from the soil all the wild beasts and all the birds. (Genesis 2.19)

Narrator: Rabbi Aha said:

Rabbi Aha: When the Holy One came to create the Earthling, the Holy One took counsel with the ministering angels, saying to them,

God: Let us make people in Our image. (Genesis 1.26)

Rabbi Aha: They asked:

Angels: What will people be like?

Rabbi Aha: God answered:

God: They will have more wisdom than you do.

Rabbi Aha: What did the Eternal do? God brought the animals, beasts, and birds before the angels and asked them:

God: What should be the name of each animal?

Rabbi Aha: But they did not know.

God: What about this one?

Rabbi Aha: And they did not know. God paraded the animals before the Earthling, and asked him:

God: What is the name of this animal?

The Earthling: An ox.

God: And of this animal?

The Earthling: A camel.

God: And of this one?

The Earthling: A donkey.

God: And of this one?

The Earthling: A horse.

Rabbi Aha: As it is written:

Torah: So Adonai, the God, formed from the soil all the wild beasts and all the birds. And brought each to the Earthling to see what the Earthling would call it. Whatever the Earthling called the animal, that became its name. (Genesis 2.20)

Rabbi Aha: Said God to the Earthling.

God: And what is your name?

Adam: I should be called Adam, because I was created from *adamah*, the ground.

Rabbi Aha: God said.

God And what is My name?

Adam: You should be called Adonai (Master), since You are Master over all Your creatures.

Narrator: Rabbi Hiyya said:

Rabbi Hiyya: That is the meaning of Isaiah 42.8:

Torah: I am Adonai (the Master), that is My name.

Rabbi Hiyya: That verse actually means, "This is My name that Adam gave Me." Then God paraded the animals again before Adam in pairs, male and female. Adam said:

Adam: Every one has a partner except me.

Rabbi Hiyya: This is what was meant in Genesis 2.20:

Torah: But for the Earthling, no helper who fit could be found.

Rabbi Hiyya: And why did God not create her for him at the beginning? Because the Holy One knew that Adam and Eve would struggle with each other. That is why God set it up so that Adam had to demand her. But as soon as he did:

Torah: Adonai, the God, made the Earthling sleep a deep sleep and took one rib and then closed in the flesh. Adonai, the God, built the rib into a woman, and brought her to the Earthling.

17

1. Why did God consult with the angels? _____

2. Why could the Earthling name the animals when the angels couldn't? ____
_____

3. According to this midrash, what do we learn from God's name? ____
_____

4. Why did God make Adam ask for a partner? _____
_____
_____

Paper-Tear Midrash

A paper tear midrash is an artistic creation made with paper and glue. No scissors, no knives, no rulers, and no pens or pencils may be used. Make your own paper tear midrash of one of the following:

- What Eve saw when she first opened her eyes.
- Adam names the animals and the birds.
- The Tree in the Middle of the Garden of Eden.
- Adam and Eve leaving the Garden of Eden.

18

Text 3

Genesis 4.1–26

Cain and Abel

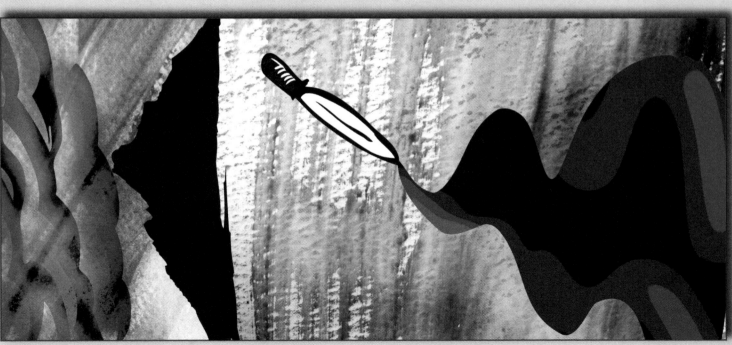

Prologue

Narrator 1: 4.1Adam knew his wife Eve. She became pregnant and gave birth to Cain. She said:

Eve: Cain means "I got a man with God's help."

Narrator 1: 2Later on she gave birth to Abel, his brother. Abel became a shepherd. Cain farmed the earth.

The Story

Narrator 2: 3When time passed, Cain brought the fruit of the earth as a gift-offering for Adonai. 4And Abel brought the best firstborn of his flock. 5Adonai accepted Abel and his gift, but Cain and his gift Adonai didn't accept.

Narrator 1: Cain grew angry. His face fell. 6Adonai said to Cain:

God: Why are you angry? Why has your face fallen? 8When you are good aren't you lifted up? But when you don't do good sin haunts your door ready to tempt you. But you can master it.

Narrator 1: [8]Cain said something to his brother Abel. When they were in the field, Cain rose up upon his brother Abel and killed him.

Narrator 2: [9]Adonai said to Cain:

God: Where is your brother Abel?

Narrator 2: He said:

Cain: I don't know. Am I my brother's keeper?

Narrator 2: [10]God said:

God: What have you done? The voice of your brother's bloods shouts to Me from the earth. [11]From now on, you are cursed from the earth because the earth opened up its mouth to take your brother's bloods from your hand. [12]From now on, when you work the earth it will no longer give you strength. You will be hunted and wander homeless over the land.

Narrator 1: [13]Cain said:

Cain: My punishment is too great to bear. [14]I have been banished today from the face of the earth, and from Your face I will be hidden as well. I will wander homeless over the land. Therefore, whomever meets me may kill me.

Narrator 1: [15]Adonai said,

God: Whoever kills Cain...will be punished.

Narrator 1: Adonai put a mark on Cain so whoever met him would know not to kill him. [16]Cain went from before God's face. He settled in the land of Nod (which means "wandering"), east of Eden.

Epilogue

Narrator 1: [17]Cain knew his woman. She got pregnant and gave birth to a son, Enoch. Cain built a town and called the name of the town like the name of his son,

Cain: Enoch.

Narrator 2: [18]Enoch fathered Irad. Irad fathered Mehuyael. Mehuyael fathered Metusael. Metusael fathered Lamekh. [19]Lamekh took two women. The first was named Adah. The second was named Tzillah. [20]Adah birthed Yaval. He was the father of those who live in tents with live-stock. [21]His brother's name was Yuval. He was the father of all who play the lyre and the pipe. [22] And Tzillah also birthed: Tuval-Cain, the one who forged bronze and iron tools, and Tuval-Cain's sister, Naamah.

Narrator 1: [23]Lamekh said to his women.

Lamekh: Adah and Tzillah listen to me. Women of Lamekh, give ear to my voice. I have killed a man for wounding me a child for bruising me. [24]Cain is to be avenged only seven times while Lamekh will be avenged seventy-seven times.

Narrator 2: [25]Adam knew his woman again. She birthed a son. She called his name:

Eve: Seth.

Narrator 1: God has put another seed in Abel's place because Cain had killed him.

Narrator 2: [26]A son was born to Seth also. He called his name Enosh. Then they began to call upon the name of Adonai.

THE CANAANITE GAZETTE

Imagine that you are a reporter for the *Canaanite Gazette*. Conduct the following interviews.

1. Ask Adam: "How are your two sons different, one from the other?"

2. Ask Eve: "How are your sons different, one from the other?"

3. Ask Abel: "How are you and your brother different?"

4. Ask Cain: "How are you and your brother different?"

5. Ask God: "Why did You accept Abel's offering and not Cain's? If You had it to do over, would You do it that way again?"

6. Ask Cain's wife: "What do you love most about your husband? What about your husband is most difficult for you?"

Midrash 1: Cain's Worst Punishment

Genesis Rabbah 22.11

Torah: "My punishment is too great to bear. I have been banished today from the face of the earth, and from Your face I will be hidden as well. I will wander homeless over the land. Therefore, whoever meets me may kill me." (Genesis 4.13-14)

Narrator: Cain said to God:

Cain: You can put up with the heavens and the earth, yet you cannot put up with my sin. My sin is greater than my father's. My father broke a small commandment and was driven out of the Garden of Eden. Mine is a far heavier crime. It is murder. My sin is much greater.

Yesterday you drove out my father, today you drive me out. You've created an empty world because from now on

Torah: "from Your face I will be hidden." (Genesis 4.13-14)

---

1. According to this Midrash, what was the worst part of Cain's punishment?

2. When we do something wrong, how are we like Cain? How is God's face hidden from us?

Midrash 2: The Mark of Cain

Genesis Rabbah 22.12

Torah: Adonai said, "Whoever kills Cain... will be punished." Adonai put a mark on Cain so whoever met him would know not to kill him. Genesis 4.15

Narrator: Rabbi Judah said:

Rabbi Judah: The cattle, beasts, and birds assembled to demand justice for Abel. Said the Holy One,

God: I say to you, "Whoever kills Cain...will be punished."

Narrator: Rabbi Nehemiah explained:

Rabbi Nehemiah: Cain's judgment shall not be as the judgment of other murderers. Cain murdered, but there is no one to learn from his punishment. But from now on, all who slay shall be slain.

Torah: Adonai put a mark on Cain so whoever met him would know not to kill him. (Genesis 4.16)

Narrator: Rabbi Judah explained the mark by saying:

Rabbi Judah: God made the sun shine for him.

Narrator: Rabbi Nehemiah said to him:

Rabbi Nehemiah: For that evil man God would not cause the sun to shine! Rather, God gave Cain leprosy.

Narrator: Rav explained the mark by saying:

Rav: God gave Cain a dog.

Narrator: Abba Yosi explained the mark by saying:

Abba Yosi: God made a horn grow out of Cain.

Narrator: Rav said:

Rav: God made Cain an example to murderers.

Narrator: Rabbi Hanin said:

Rabbi Hanin: God made Cain an example to people who repent.

Continued on page 24

23

1. Who demanded Cain's death?

_____

2. According to Rabbi Neḥemiah, why wasn't Cain put to death?

_____

3. What was the mark of Cain supposed to do?

_____

4. Why would the shining sun be a good mark for Cain?

_____

5. Why would leprosy be a good mark for Cain?

_____

6. Why would a dog be a good mark for Cain?

_____

7. Why would a horn be a good mark for Cain?

_____

8. What makes Cain an example for would-be murderers?

_____

9. What makes Cain a role model for people who need to repent?

_____

Postcards From Cain

Imagine that the whole story is over.

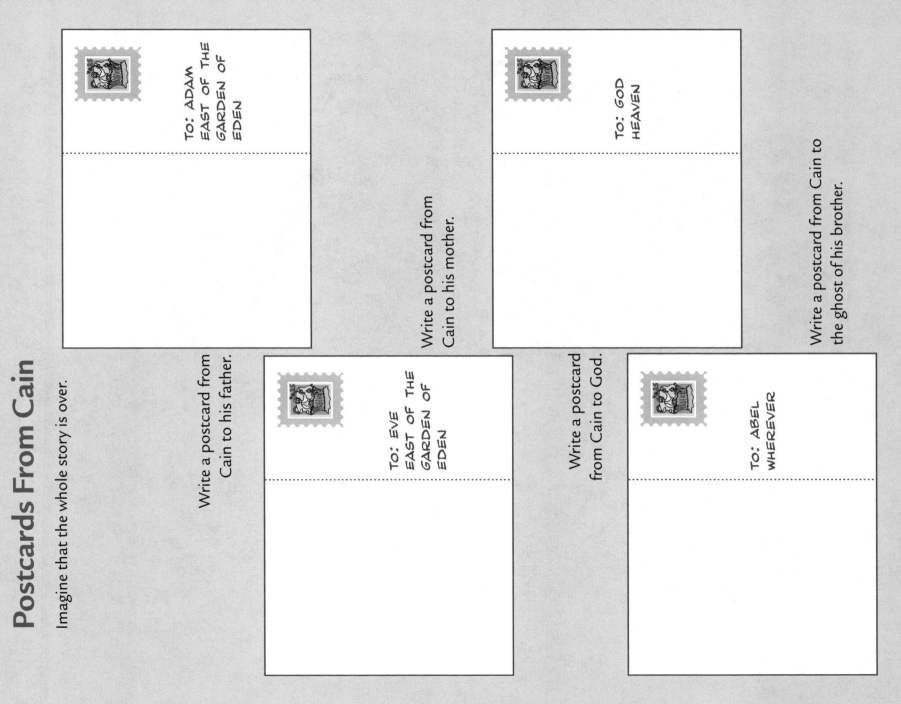

TO: ADAM
EAST OF THE
GARDEN OF
EDEN

TO: EVE
EAST OF THE
GARDEN OF
EDEN

TO: GOD
HEAVEN

TO: ABEL
WHEREVER

Write a postcard from Cain to his father.

Write a postcard from Cain to his mother.

Write a postcard from Cain to God.

Write a postcard from Cain to the ghost of his brother.

The Flood

And Introducing Noah

Narrator 1: 6-5Adonai saw that people did a lot of evil on the land. All the urges of their hearts' thoughts were evil all day long. 6Adonai was uncomfortable about having made people. God's heart was pained. Adonai said:

God: 7I will wipe people—whom I have created—off the face of the earth. People and beasts and crawling things and sky birds—I'm uncomfortable that I made them.

Narrator 1: 8But Noah (meaning "comfort") found favor in Adonai's eyes.

Narrator 2: 9This is the family history of Noah. Noah was a righteous person, wholesome for his generation. Noah walked with God. 10Noah fathered three sons: Shem, Ham, and Yafet. 11The land was being destroyed before God. The land was filled with violence. 12God saw the land:

God: *Hinnei.* It has been destroyed, because each living thing had destroyed its way of living on the earth.

Narrator 2: [13]God said to Noah:

God: Before My face the end of all flesh unavoidable, because the land is filled with violence before them. *Hinnei.* I am ready to destroy the land.

[14]Make yourself a wooden ark. Make it with rooms and cover it inside and out with tar. [15]This is how you will make it:

300 cubits long, 50 cubits wide, 30 cubits high. [16]Make an opening for light one cubit below the top. Make an opening in the ark's side. Make it with a bottom deck, a second deck, and a third deck.

Hinnei. I am bringing a flood of water on the land to destroy all flesh under the skies with breath of life in it. Everything on earth shall pass away. [18]But I will set up My covenant with you. You shall come into the ark, you, your sons, your wife and your sons' wives with you. [19]Of all that lives, of all flesh, you shall bring two of each into the ark to keep it alive with you. Let them be male and female. [20]Two of each shall come to you to keep it alive.

Narrator1: [22]Noah did all that God commanded him. He did it.

The Water's Rise

Narrator 2: [7.1]Adonai said to Noah:

God: Come, you and all your household, into the ark. For I have seen that you are the righteous one before Me in this generation.

[2]Take with you seven pairs of every clean animal—a male and his female. And from every non-clean animal take two—a male and his female. [3]Also, from every sky bird, take with you seven pairs of every clean animal—a male and his female—to keep species alive on the face of all the land.

[4]Because 7 days from now I will make it rain upon the land for 40 days and 40 nights. I will wipe all established things that I have made off the face of the earth.

Narrator 1: [5]And Noah did all that Adonai commanded.

27

Narrator 2: [6]Noah was 600 years old when the flood came and water was upon the land.

Narrator 1: [7]Noah and his sons, and his wife, and his sons' wives came into the ark away from the face of the flood.

Narrator 2: [8]Of every clean animal, of every animal which is not clean, of birds, and of each thing that creeps on the ground—[9]two by two they came to Noah, to the ark. They came male and female, just as God commanded him.

Narrator 1: [10]Seven days later the waters of the flood were over all the earth.

Narrator 2: [11]All the waters came up from the springs of the deepest places. The floodgates of the sky broke open.

Narrator 1: [12]The rain fell on the land for 40 days and 40 nights.

Narrator 2: [13]On that day Noah and Shem, Ham, and Yafet, the sons of Noah and Noah's wife, and his sons' three wives with them came into the ark. [15]Into the ark, two by two, came all living things that had the breath of life—[16]just as God had commanded.

Narrator 1: Then, Adonai closed him in.

[17]The flood was on the face of the land for 40 days. The waters grew and lifted the ark from on the land. [18]The waters swelled and grew very much on the land. The ark floated on the face of the waters. [19]The waters swelled and increased over the earth. All the high mountains that were under all the skies were covered.

Narrator 2: [21]Death came to all life, those that crawled on the land, the birds, the cattle, the wild animals, the swarming things that swarmed on the land—and all people.

Narrator 1: [22]Everything that had the breath of life in it, that was on dry land, died.

Narrator 2: [24]The waters swelled for 150 days.

The Waters Recede

Narrator 2: [8:1]God remembered Noah and all the living things and all the animals that were with him in the ark. God brought a breath of wind across the land and the water went down. [2]The springs of the deepest places and the floodgates of the sky were closed.

Narrator 1: The rain from the sky stopped. [3]The waters returned from covering the land. They were constantly moving and returning.

Narrator 2: After 150 days, there was less water. [4]The ark came to rest on the mountains of Ararat. [5]The water kept moving and receding until the tops of the mountains could be seen.

Narrator 1: [6]After 40 days, Noah opened the window in the ark which he had made. [7]He sent out a raven.

Narrator 2: [7]The raven kept leaving and returning until the waters dried from off of the land.

Narrator 1: [8]Then he sent out a dove to see if there was still water on the face of the earth. [9]But the dove could not find a place to rest her feet so she returned to him. (The waters were still on the face of the earth.) He stuck out his hand and took her and brought her to him into the ark. [10]He waited another seven days and again sent the dove from the ark.

[11]The dove came to him in the evening. In her beak there were fresh olive leaves. This is how Noah knew that the waters had gone down from on the land. [12]He waited another seven days further, and then he sent out the dove, but she returned to him no more. [13]When Noah took the covering off of the ark, he saw that the face of the earth was firm.

Narrator 2: [14]The land was dry. God spoke to Noah:

God: [16]Go out of the ark. You and your wife and your sons and your son's wives with you. Bring living things that are with you—all life: birds, animals and all crawling things, that they can be fruitful and become many on the earth.

Narrator 2: [18]So Noah and his sons, and his wife and his sons' wives went out of the ark. [19]All living things came out of the ark by families.

29

Narrator 1: ²⁰Noah built an altar to Adonai. He took from every clean animal and from every clean bird and burnt offerings on the altar. ²¹Adonai smelled the comforting smell and it was said in Adonai's heart:

God: I will never again curse the soil because of people, because the urges of their hearts are evil from their youth. I will never again wipe out all living things. ²²Never again in all the earth's days will seeding time and harvest time, cold and heat, summer and winter, day and night, come to an end.

Narrator 2: ⁹¹God blessed Noah and his sons, saying:

God: Be fruitful and become many, and fill the land. ²All life on the earth, every bird of the sky, all that creeps on the soil, every fish of the sea shall fear you and be terrified of you, because I put them into your hands. ³Just like the green plants, I now give you all moving life to eat. ⁴But you must not eat the flesh together with the soul-blood. ⁵As for your soul-blood, I will seek responsibility from every person for the life of his or her brother or sister. ⁶Whoever sheds the blood of a person by a person shall his blood be shed, because God created people in God's image.

⁷Be fruitful and become many, and fill the earth, and become many on it.

The Covenant

Narrator 2: ⁸God said to Noah and to his sons with him:

God: ⁹Hineni, I now establish my covenant with you and with your future-family after you and with every living thing that was with you...that went off the ark—with all life on the land. I will establish my covenant with you. Never again will all life be wiped out by the waters of a flood. Never again will there be a flood to destroy the land.

Narrator 2: ¹²Then God said:

God: This is a sign of the covenant that I give between Me and you, and with all the living things with you for all generations to come. ¹³I give my rainbow in the clouds, which will be the sign of the covenant between Me and the land. ¹⁴Whenever I fill the skies with clouds—whenever a rainbow appears in those clouds—¹⁵I will remember My covenant. Never again will waters become a flood to destroy all life.

30

16When the rainbow is in the clouds I will look at it and remember my everlasting covenant.

Narrator 2: 17God said to Noah:

God: That is the sign of the covenant which I established between Me and between all life which is on the land.

THE CANAANITE GAZETTE

Imagine that you are a reporter for the *Canaanite Gazette.* Conduct the following interviews.

1. Ask God: "What did you see Noah doing (as compared to what you saw other people doing) that made you comfortable with him?"

2. Ask Noah: "Why do you think God picked you? What makes you different?"

3. Ask Noah's sons: "What was it like being part of the only 'righteous family' in the neighborhood?"

4. Ask Noah's wife: "How do you feel about all the work it takes to save the world?"

5. Ask any animal: "Tell the story of the flood from your perspective."

Pirke de Rabbi Eliezer 23

Rabbi Tanḥuma: It took Noah fifty-two years to build the ark. It took that long to give people a chance to repent. But they did not repent.

Z'vakhim 113b

Rabbi Yoḥanan: In my opinion the flood did not reach *Eretz Yisrael*.

Rabbi Ḥisda: In the generation of the flood the decree of destruction was not decreed against the fish in the sea, because it teaches in Genesis 7.22:

Torah: Everything that had the breath of life in it, that was on dry land, died.

Rabbi Ḥisda: The *Re'im*, giant animals, stayed in *Eretz Yisrael*.

Rabbi Yannai: It did reach *Eretz Yisrael*. They took the young of the *Re'im* into the ark.

Rabbah ben Bar Ḥanah: I saw a sea *Re'im*, one day old, which was as big as Mount Tabor.

Another Rabbi: It was so big that they took only the tip of its nose into the ark.

Rabbi Yoḥanan: They took only its head into the ark.

Resh Lakish: The ark plunged up and down but they tied its horns to the ark to keep it attached.

Rabbi Ḥisda: The people in the generation of the flood sinned with hot passion, and with hot water they were punished. But a miracle was performed for the water, and it was cooled at the side of the ark.

Pirke de Rabbi Eliezer 23

Rabbi Tzadok: All the living things that were on the face of the earth were destroyed as it is taught in Genesis 7.22:

Torah: Everything that had the breath of life in it, that was on dry land, died.

Rabbi Tzadok: The only ones left alive were Noah and his family. We also learn that from Genesis 7:22:

Torah: Only Noah survived and those with him in the ark.

Rabbi Tzadok: The other exception was Og, King of Bashan. He clung on pegs and a board on the outside of the ark. He swore to Noah that he and his children would always serve Noah's family. What did Noah do? He cut a hole in the ark and passed out food every day. We know this because Deuteronomy 3:2 teaches:

Torah: Og, King of Bashan, was the last surviving giant.

Questions

1. What is a *Re'im*?

_____

_____

2. Which of these images about the *Re'im* is your favorite?

_____

_____

3. What lesson does it teach?

_____

4. If Noah saved a person (Og, King of Bashan) from the flood, what can we learn about Noah?

_____

_____

5. What is the lesson of the "Og" story?

_____

_____

33

Make a Midrash

Write a set of rules for the Ark.

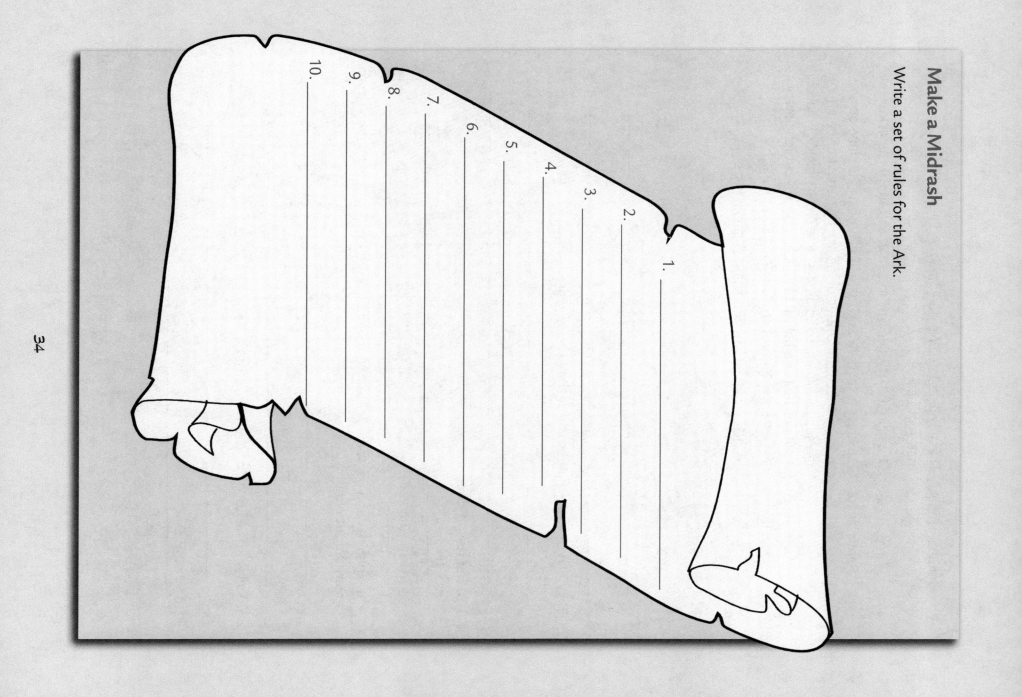

1.

2.

3.

4.

5.

6.

7.

8.

9.

10.

Text 5 The Tower of Babel
Genesis 11.1–9

Narrator 1: 11.1And it was that all the earth had one language and had one set of words. ²People traveled to the east that they found themselves in a valley in the Land of Shinar and settled there.

Narrator 2: ³People said to their neighbors:

People: Let us make bricks and burn them hard.

Narrator 1: For them, bricks were stones. For them, clay was cement. ⁴Then they said:

People: Let us build a city and a tower with its top in the sky. Let us make a name for ourselves, to keep us from being scattered over the face of all the land.

Narrator 2: ⁵Adonai came down to see the city and the tower that the children of Adam were building. ⁶Adonai said:

God: Now they are one people with one language for all. This is only the beginning of what they will do. From now on, there will be no limits. They will do whatever they feel like doing. ⁷Let us go

THE CANAANITE GAZETTE

Imagine that you are a reporter for the *Canaanite Gazette*. Conduct the following interviews.

1. Ask the leader of the building project: "You said, 'Let us make a name for ourselves, to keep us from being scattered over the face of all the land.' Why were you afraid that you would be scattered?"

2. Ask God: "What were You afraid of? What would have been so bad if the people had built a tower which reached to the heavens? You don't live in heaven, do You?"

3. Ask a builder or two or three: "Now that your language has been babbled, which words that you now use are the same or similar to the original words in the one language?"

4. Ask a child of a builder, "When your mother told you the story of the Tower of Babel, how did she explain the end of the building project?"

Narrator 1: [8]So Adonai scattered them from there over the face of all the land and they stopped building the city. [9]That is why the city is called Babel, because there Adonai babbled the language of all the land. And from there, Adonai scattered them over the face of all the land.

down and babble their language so that no one will hear another's language.

The Story of a Coat

Pirkei de Rabbi Eliezer 24

Narrator: Rabbi Akiva said:

Rabbi Akiva: People abandoned the Rule of Heaven and appointed one of their own, Nimrod, to be king. He was the slave son of a slave.

Narrator: Rabbi Hanina said:

Rabbi Hanina: Nimrod was a mighty hero.

Narrator: Rabbi Yehudah said:

Rabbi Yehudah: The coats that the Holy One made for Adam and Eve were with Noah on the ark. Ham, the son of Noah, passed them on to Nimrod. When he put them on, all the beasts and animals, bowed before him. When people saw the power he had over animals, they made him king, believing the power was in him. We learn this from Genesis 10:9:

Torah: Nimrod was a mighty hunter.

Note: *According to other midrashim, God made Adam and Eve's coats out of snake skin so that no animal had to die to keep them warm. God made it so that Adam and Eve were protected from wild animals by patterns embedded in the skins. Noah and his family used these coats to control the animals on the ark.*

Rabbi Yehudah: Nimrod said to his people:

Nimrod: Let us build a city and a tower with its top in the sky. Let us make a name for ourselves, to keep us from being scattered over the face of all the land. (Genesis 11:4)

Rabbi Phineas: There were no stones where they wanted to build the city and the tower. What did they do? They baked bricks. The workers took the bricks up the eastern staircase and then came down the southern staircase. If a worker fell and died, no one noticed. But if a brick fell they sat down and cried.

Abraham, the son of Terah, passed by and saw them building the city and the tower. He told them that their work was not in God's name. But the workers rejected his words.

Narrator: Rabbi Simeon said:

37

Rabbi Simeon: When they wished to talk to each other they could no longer speak the same language. What did they do? Each one took a sword and tried to destroy each other. That is why:

Torah: That is why the city is called Babel, because there Adonai babbled the language of all the land. Adonai scattered them over the face of all the land. (Genesis 11.9)

Narrator: Rabbi Meir said:

Rabbi Meir: Esau, the brother of Jacob, saw the coats of Nimrod that the Holy One had made for Adam and Eve, and he coveted them. Esau stole them for himself.

When Esau put these coats on, he too, became a mighty hero and a hunter.

When Jacob left home he wore these coats. He buried these coats and said,

Jacob: The wicked Esau is not worthy to wear these coats.

Note: According to other midrishim, when Rebekkah dressed Jacob in Esau's clothes and tied skins on his hands to fool Isaac, his father, it was these clothes he put on. They were left with Rebekkah by Esau because he thought her tent was a good place to hide stolen property. If someone came looking for them, he would not be blamed.

38

Questions

1. What did the coats do for Adam and Eve?

_____

_____

2. What did they do for Noah's family?

_____

_____

3. What did they do for Nimrod?

_____

_____

4. What did they do for Esau?

_____

_____

5. Who made the coats?

_____

_____

6. Which uses of the coats were good? Which were evil?

_____

_____

7. How was the tower like the coats?

_____

_____

8. What's the lesson of this story?

_____

_____

Write a Tower Midrash

Write a conversation between two workers on the tower. Have it start as a ordinary conversation between two people talking while they work. Have it continue through the moment when God babbled the language of everyone there.

Text 6
Genesis 10.1, 11.10–12.9

Abram & Sarai Come to Canaan

The back story

Narrator 1: ^{10.1}Noah fathered three sons: Shem, Ham and Yafet. They in turn fathered sons after the flood.

Narrator 2: ^{11.10}This is the family history of Shem. Shem was one hundred years old when he fathered Arpachshad two years after the flood.

Narrator 1: ¹²Arpachshad fathered Shelah.

Narrator 2: ¹⁴Shelah fathered Eber.

Narrator 1: ¹⁶Eber fathered Peleg.

Narrator 2: ¹⁸Peleg fathered Reu.

Narrator 1: ²⁰Reu fathered Serug.

Narrator 2: ²²Serug fathered Nahor.

Narrator 1: ²⁴Nahor fathered Terah. ²⁶When Terah was seventy years old, he fathered Abram, Nahor and Haran.

Narrator 2: ²⁷This is the family history of Teraḥ.

Teraḥ fathered Abram, Naḥor and Haran. Haran fathered Lot.
²⁸Haran died before his father, in the land of his birth, Ur Kasdim.
²⁹Both Abram and Naḥor married. Abram's wife was named Sarai.
The name of Naḥor's wife was Milcah, who was the daughter of
Haran, who was the father of Milcah and Iscah. ³⁰Sarai was barren,
she had no child.

Narrator 1: ³¹Teraḥ took Abram, his son, and Lot, son of Haran, his grandson,
and Sarai, his daughter-in-law, Abram's wife. Together they left Ur
Kasdim to go to the land of Canaan. They went as far as Haran and
settled there. ³²Teraḥ lived 205 years. Teraḥ died in Haran (long after
his son Abram had left).

The Moment

Narrator 2: ¹²⁻¹Adonai said to Abram:

God: Take yourself from your land, from your birthplace, from your
father's house, to the land: There I will let you see.

²And I will make you a great nation. And I will bless you. And I will
make your name great. And you will be a blessing. ³And I will bless
those who bless you. And I will curse anyone who curses you. All the
families of the earth will be blessed through you.

Narrator 2: ⁴Abram went as Adonai had told him. And Lot went with him.
Abram was 75 years old when he left Haran. ⁵Abram took Sarai his
wife and Lot his nephew, and all they owned, and all their people
who they amassed in Haran, and they left to go to the land of
Canaan.

Narrator 1: They came to the land of Canaan. ⁶Abram crossed the land to the
place of Shechem, to the Oak of Moreh. The Canaanites were then
living in the land. ⁷Adonai was seen by Abram and said:

God: To your future-family I will give this land.

Narrrator 1:   And he built an altar there, to Adonai, Who had been seen by him. ⁸From there he moved on to the hills east of Beth El. He spread his tent with Beth El seaward and Ai towards sunrise. He built an altar there to Adonai. He called on the name of Adonai. ⁹Abram traveled, stage-by-stage southward, towards the Negev.

THE CANAANITE GAZETTE

Imagine that you are a reporter for the *Canaanite Gazette*. Conduct the following interviews.

1. Ask Abram: "In the Torah, nothing is said about (A) your journey to Canaan, and (B) your entry into the land. Tell us what happened."

2. Ask Sarai the same question.

3. Ask Lot the same question.

4. Ask God: "What made you decide that you wanted to give one family a lot of extra attention, and what made you think that Sarai and Abram's family should be that family?

The Death of Haran

Genesis Rabbah 38.13

Torah: Haran died before his father, in the land of his birth, Ur Kasdim. (Genesis 11.28)

Narrator: Rabbi Ḥiyya said:

Rabbi Ḥiyya: Teraḥ made idols. He once went away somewhere and left Abram to sell them. A man came and wished to buy one.

Rabbi Ḥiyya: Abram asked him:

Abraham: How old are you?

Rabbi Ḥiyya: The man answered:

Man: Fifty years.

Abraham: What kind of man are you? You are fifty years old and you are ready to worship a day-old object!

Rabbi Ḥiyya: At this the man became ashamed and left.

Another time a woman came with a plateful of flour and asked him:

Woman: Take this and offer it to the idols.

Rabbi Ḥiyya: So he took a stick, broke the idols, and put the stick in the hand of the largest. When his father returned he demanded:

Teraḥ: What have you done to them?

Rabbi Ḥiyya: Abram answered:

Abram: I cannot hide the truth from you. A woman came with a plateful of fine meal and asked me to offer it to them. One argued, "I must eat first," while another argued, "I must eat first." Then the largest got up, took the stick, and broke the others.

Rabbi Ḥiyya: Teraḥ shouted:

Teraḥ: Why do you make fun of me? Do idols know anything?

Rabbi Ḥiyya: Abram answered him:

Abram: Father, your ears should listen to what your mouth is saying.

Rabbi Ḥiyya: Teraḥ seized him and delivered Abram to the king, Nimrod. Nimrod said:

Nimrod: Let us worship the fire!

Rabbi Hiyya: Abram answered:

Abram: No! Let's worship water that extinguishes the fire.

Rabbi Hiyya: Nimrod said:

Nimrod: Then let's worship water!

Rabbi Hiyya: Abram came back:

Abram: No! Let's worship the clouds that carry the water.

Nimrod: Then let us worship the clouds!

Rabbi Hiyya: Abram came back:

Abram: No! Let's worship the winds that move the clouds.

Nimrod: Then let us worship the wind!

Abram: No! Let's worship people who can withstand the wind.

Nimrod: You are just messing with words. We will worship nothing but the fire. But I will throw you into it, and let your God that you love come and save you.

Rabbi Hiyya: Haran was standing there undecided.

Haran: If Abram wins, I will say that I am of Abram's belief. But, if Nimrod wins, I will say that I am on Nimrod's side.

Rabbi Hiyya: When Abram came out of the fiery furnace and was saved, Nimrod asked Haran:

Nimrod: Whose belief do you follow?

Rabbi Hiyya: Haran answered:

Haran: Abram's.

Rabbi Hiyya: Immediately Nimrod grabbed Haran and threw him into the fire. His innards were roasted and he died before his father. That is why Genesis 11.28 says:

Torah: Haran died before his father, in the land of his birth, Ur Kasdim.

45

1. What does this midrash teach about idolatry?

_____

_____

_____

2. What does this midrash teach about animism (the belief that parts of nature are gods)?

_____

_____

_____

3. How does this midrash explain that "Haran died beore his father?"

_____

_____

_____

_____

Make a Midrash

Write the Abram, Sarai, or Lot diary entry for the day they left home and headed towards the land of Canaan.

Dear Diary,

_____

_____

_____

_____

_____

_____

_____

_____

_____

_____

_____

_____

_____

Signed _____
(Abram, Sarai or Lot)

Abram: Lot Leaves

The Return

Narrator 1: ¹³·¹ Abram went up from Egypt, he, his wife, and all he had, and Lot with him, to the Negev. ² Abram was heavy with livestock, silver and gold.

³ He went by stages from the Negev to Beth El, to the place where his tent had been at the beginning, between Beth El and Ai, ⁴ to the place where he had first made the altar. There Abram called upon the name of Adonai.

Narrator 2: ⁵ And Lot, who went with Abram, had sheep, cattle, and tents. The land could not support both of them settling together. ⁶ They had so many belongings that they were not able to settle together.

Narrator 1: ⁷ There was feuding between Abram's herdsmen and Lot's herdsmen. (At that time, the Canaanites and Perizzites were settled in the land).

THE CANAANITE GAZETTE

Imagine that you are a reporter for the *Canaanite Gazette*. Conduct the following interviews.

1. Ask Lot: "What was life like in the family after you came back from Egypt."

2. Ask Lot's shepherds: "What were the arguments really about?

3. Ask Abram's shepherds: "What were the arguments really about?"

4. Ask Sarai, "How did you feel when Lot left?"

The Settlement

Narrator 1: [8] Abram said to Lot:

Abram: Please, let there be no feud between me and you, between my herdsmen and between your herdsmen, because we are men who are like brothers. [9] The whole land is before you—please separate from me. If you go to the left, I will go to the right. If you go to the right, I will go to the left.

The Foreshadowing

Narrator 1: [10] Lot lifted up his eyes and saw the plain of the Jordan. It was land with much water before God destroyed Sodom and Gemorah. It was like God's garden. It was like Egypt up to Zoar. [11] So Lot chose the Jordan plain and journeyed eastward. So they were separated, each man from his brother.

Narrator 2: [12] Abram settled in the land of Canaan. Lot settled in the cities of the plain and pitched his tents near Sodom. [13] The men of Sodom were evil and sinned on purpose.

The Blessing

Narrator 2: [14] Adonai said to Abram after Lot was separated from him:

God: Lift up your eyes and look around. North, South to the Negev, East to sunrise and West to the sea. [15] All the land which you see, I give to you and your future-family forever. [16] Your future-family will be like dust covering the land. Like the dust of the land, your future-family will be impossible to count. [17] Get up and walk the land from end to end and from side to side—because I give it to you.

Narrator 2: [18] Abram moved his tents and settled near Hebron. There he built an altar to Adonai.

49

The Herdsmen's Battle

Genesis Rabbah 41.5

Torah: There was feuding between Abram's herdsmen and Lot's herdsmen. (Genesis 13.7)

Narrator: Rabbi Berekiah said in Rabbi Yudan's name:

Rabbi Berekiah: Abram's cattle used to go out muzzled, but Lot's did not go out muzzled. Said Abram's herdsmen to them:

Abram's Shepherds: Is robbery now legal?

Rabbi Berekiah: Lot's herdsmen replied:

Lot's Shepherds: The Holy One said to Abram:

God: To your future-family I will give this land. (Genesis 12.7)

Lot's Shepherds: You know that Abram is as barren as a mule. He cannot have children. That makes Lot his heir. If Lot's herds graze in Canaan, they are grazing off of his land.

Narrator: Said the Holy One to them:

God: I did say to Abram:

To your future-family I have given this land. (Genesis 15.18)

When will he get the land? When the seven nations that live there now are uprooted from it. Now, however.

At that time, the Canaanites and Perizzites were settled in the land. (Genesis 13.7)

At the moment they still own the land.

50

Questions

1. According to this midrash, what was the reason for the argument?

_____

_____

_____

2. Why did Lot's shepherds feel entitled to graze their sheep on the land?

_____

_____

_____

3. Why did Abram's shepherds refuse to graze their sheep?

_____

_____

_____

4. What are two lessons of this midrash?

_____

_____

_____

_____

Sheep Talk

Write a conversation between one of Abram's sheep and one of Lot's. Have them tell the story of the breakup from their perspective.

Text 8
Genesis 16.1–16

Sarai, Abram & Hagar

Narrator 1: [16.1]Sarai, Abram's wife, had borne him no children. She had an Egyptian servant whose name was Hagar. [2]Sarai said to Abram:

Sarai: Behold now, Adonai has kept me from bearing children. Go with my maid. Maybe I can have children through her.

Narrator 2: Abram listened to the voice of Sarai. [3]Sarai, Abram's wife, took Hagar the Egyptian, her servant, (after Abram had been living in the land of Canaan for ten years) and gave her to Abram, her husband, as his wife. [4]He went with Hagar, and she conceived. When Hagar saw that she had conceived, she looked down on her mistress.

[5]Sarai said to Abram:

Sarai: You've wronged me. I gave my maid to you and when she saw that she had conceived she looked down on me. May Adonai judge between you and me!

Narrator 1: [6]But Abram said to Sarai:

THE CANAANITE GAZETTE

Imagine that you are a reporter for the *Canaanite Gazette*. Conduct the following interviews.

1. Ask Sarai, "How does it feel not to have children?"

2. Ask Hagar, "What was Sarai like as a boss before she sent you to Abram?"

3. Ask Abram, "What was it like to be caught between Sarai and Hagar?"

4. Ask the Angel, "Tell us about God's plans for Hagar?"

Abram: *Hinnei*, your maid is in your hands. Do with her as you please.

Narrator 2: Then Sarai dealt harshly with her, and she fled from her face. [7]Adonai's angel found her by a spring of water in the wilderness. [8]He said:

Angel: Hagar, maid of Sarai, where have you come from and where are you going?

Hagar: I am fleeing from the face of my mistress Sarai.

Narrator 1: [9]Adonai's angel said to her:

Angel: Return to your mistress, and submit to her.

Narrator 2: [10]Adonai's angel also said to her,

Angel: I will greatly multiply your future-family that they cannot be counted because they are too many.

Narrator 1: [11]Adonai's Angel said to her:

Angel: Behold, you are pregnant and shall bear a son. You shall call his name Ishmael (meaning God heard) because Adonai has heard your suffering. [12]He shall be a wild ass of a man. His hand will be against every man and every man's hand will be against him. He shall dwell among all of his kinsmen.

Narrator 2: [13]She called on the name of Adonai who had spoken to her:

Hagar: You are a God of seeing. Have I really seen God who sees me?

Narrator 1: [14]Therefore the well was called Beer-la-ḥai-roi. It lies between Kadesh and Bered. Hagar bore Abram a son. [15]Abram called the name of his son, whom Hagar bore:

Abram: Ishmael.

Narrator 2: Abram was eighty-six years old when Hagar bore Ishmael.

Hagar's Story
Genesis Rabbah 45.1

Narrator: Rabbi Simeon bar Yohai said:

Rabbi Simeon bar Yohai: Hagar was Pharaoh's daughter. When Pharaoh saw what was done on Sarai's behalf in his own house, Pharaoh took his daughter and gave her to Sarai, saying:

Pharaoh: It is better to have my daughter be a handmaid in this house than the mistress of another house.

Rabbi Simeon bar Yohai: This is the story behind:

Torah: She had an Egyptian servant whose name was Hagar. (Genesis 16.1)

Narrator: Pharaoh was saying to Sarai:

Pharaoh: Here is your "agar" (meaning reward).

Narrator: Abimelech, the King of Gerar, when he saw the miracles performed in his house on Sarai's behalf, also gave his daughter to her, saying:

Abimelech: It is better to have my daughter be a handmaid in this house than the mistress of another house.

Rabbi Simeon bar Yohai: This is the story behind:

Torah: Kings' daughters are among your favorites: (Psalms 45.10)

Narrator: This verse teaches about the daughters of two kings who served Sarai. This verse continues:

Torah: At your right hand stands the queen in gold of Ophir.

Narrator: This is talking about Sarai.

55

Questions

1. Do you know what Sarai means? We will learn its meaning in a midrash in the next chapter.

_____

_____

2. According to this midrash, who was Hagar?

_____

_____

3. If Hagar was a princess, why was she a servant to Sarah?

_____

_____

4. What is the story of Abimelech's daughter?

_____

_____

5. What does this midrash teach us about the arguments between Sarai and Hagar?

_____

_____

Write a postcard
from Hagar to
her father telling
what it was like
being a servant
to Sarai.

To:
Pharaoh
Egypt

Hagar
Canaan

Write a return
postcard from
Pharaoh to Hagar
making suggestions
about how she
should act.

Abram Becomes Abraham

Narrator 1: 17:1When Abram was 99 years old, Adonai appeared to Abram and said to him:

God: I am God, Shaddai. Walk before me and be the best. 2I put my covenant between Me and you. I will make you very, very many.

Narrator 2: 3Abram bowed to the ground. God spoke with him:

God: 4As for me, here is my covenant with you—you will become the father of many nations. 5No longer will your name be called Abram. Instead your name will be Abraham for I will make you *Av Hamon Goyyim* (the father of many nations). 6Many nations and rulers will come from you.

7I set up My covenant for Me and for you and your future-family after you. It is an everlasting covenant. I will be God to you and to your future-family. 8I will give to you and to your future-family, the land where you are staying. All the land of Canaan will be yours forever.

THE CANAANITE GAZETTE

Imagine that you are a reporter for the *Canaanite Gazette*. Conduct the following interviews.

1. Ask Abraham: "What was it like to talk to God? How do you feel about the promises that God made to you?"

2. Ask Sarah: "How do you feel about your new name? How do you feel about God's promises?"

3. Ask Ishmael: "How do you feel about your father and his God?"

4. Ask Hagar: "How did you feel about your son's circumcision?"

Narrator 1: [9]God said to Abraham:

God: As for you, you are to keep my covenant, you and your future-family. [10]This is my covenant. Circumcise every male. That will be the sign of the covenant between Me and between you. [12]When eight days old, every boy should be circumcised.

Narrator 2: [15]God said to Abraham:

God: As for Sarai your wife, don't call her Sarai anymore, because Sarah (meaning "princess") is now her name. [16]I will bless her and I will give you a son from her. I will bless her, and nations and rulers will come from her

Narrator 1: [17]Abraham fell to the ground laughing. He thought:

Abraham: How is a 100-year-old man going to father a son? How is 90-year-old Sarah going to give birth?"

Narrator 2: [18]Abraham said to God:

Abraham: If only Ishmael would live before you.

God: [19]Sarah, your wife, will yet give birth to a son. You will name him Isaac (meaning "he laughs"). I will set up my covenant with him as an everlasting covenant.

[20]As for Ishmael, I hear you. I bless him. I will make him fruitful. I will make him very very many. He will father twelve princes. I will make a great nation of him.

[21]But My covenant I will set up with Isaac.

Narrator: [22]When God finished speaking with him God went up from Abraham. [23]Abraham took Ishmael, his son, and all the males among Abraham's household, and circumcised them. Abraham was 99 years old when he was circumcised. Ishmael was 13 years old when he was circumcised. On that very day, Abraham, Ishmael his son, and all of his household were circumcised.

Genesis Rabbah 47:1

Torah: As for Sarai your wife, don't call her Sarai anymore, because Sarah is now her name. I will bless her and I will give you a son from her. I will bless her and nations and rulers will come from her. (Genesis 17:15–17:16)

Narrator: It is written in Proverbs 12:4:

Torah: A virtuous woman is a crown to her husband.

Narrator: Rabbi Aha said:

Rabbi Aha: Her husband was crowned through her, but she was not crowned through her husband.

Narrator: The Rabbis said:

Rabbis: She was her husband's ruler. Usually, the husband gives orders, whereas here we read in Genesis 21:12:

Torah: In all that Sarah says to you, listen to her voice.

Torah: As for יְשָׂרַי (Sarai), your wife, don't call her Sarai anymore, because שָׂרָה (Sarah) is now her name. Genesis 17:15

Narrator: Rabbi Yehoshua ben Karhah said:

Rabbi Yehoshua: The י (*yud*) that the Eternal took from Sarai soared aloft before God and protested:

Yud: Sovereign of the Universe! I am the smallest of all letters, and now You have taken me from the name of this righteous woman!

Narrator: Said the Holy One:

God: Up to now you were in a name and the last of its letters; now I will put you in a name and at the beginning of its letters. As it says in Numbers 13:16:

Torah: And Moses called הוֹשֵׁעַ (Hoshea), the son of Nun, יְהוֹשֻׁעַ (Yehoshua).

Narrator: Rabbi Mana said:

Rabbi Mana: Formerly she was a princess [שָׂרַי] to her own people only.
Whereas now she became a princess [שָׂרָה] to all of humanity.

Questions

1. How does the Torah explain the meaning of Sarai's name change into Sarah?

_____

_____

_____

2. How was Abraham crowned through Sarai?

_____

_____

_____

3. How does the midrash explain the meaning of Sarai's name change?

_____

_____

_____

4. What do these midrashim teach us about Sarah?

_____

_____

_____

Sarah's Name Plate

Design a ceramic sign (a plaque or nameplate) for Sarah to celebrate her new name. Write a narrative describing the meaning of each of the symbols you use.

Text 10
Genesis 18.1–12

Sarah Laughed

Narrator 1: [18:1]Now Adonai appeared to Abraham by the oaks of Mamre. He was sitting at the entrance of the tent during the heat of the day. [2]He lifted his eyes and saw and *hinnei* suddenly three men were standing over him. He saw them and ran toward them. He bowed to the ground and said:

Abraham: [3]My masters, please, if I have found favor in your eyes, please do not pass by me. [4]Please let me bring you a little water. Wash your feet and rest under the tree. [5]Let me bring you some bread.

Visitors: Do just what you have said.

Narrator 2: [6]Abraham hurried into Sarah's tent.

Abraham: Hurry, three measures of good flour. Knead it and bake bread.

THE CANAANITE GAZETTE

Imagine that you are a reporter for the *Canaanite Gazette*. Conduct the following interviews.

1. Ask one of the visitors to tell you about Abraham and Sarah.

2. Ask Abraham: "How did you feel about Sarah laughing at the promise?"

3. Ask Sarah: "How did you feel when God pointed out your laughing?"

Narrator 1: [7]Abraham ran to the herd. He took a tender calf and gave it to a servant, so that he could hurry to prepare it. [8]He took yogurt and milk and the calf that had been cooked, and served to them. He stood by them under the tree while they ate.

Visitors: [9]"Where is Sarah, your wife?"

Abraham: Right here in the tent.

Voice 1: [10]I will definitely return at the time of birth, when Sarah your wife will have a son.

Narrator 2: Sarah was listening at the entrance to the tent. [11]Abraham and Sarah were old. Sarah was too old to have a child. [12]Sarah laughed and said to herself:

Sarah: Now that my time has passed, how can my old husband and I have a child?

Narrator 1: [13]Adonai said to Abraham:

God: Why is Sarah laughing and saying, "Will I really give birth, now that I am old?" [14]Is any miracle too great for Adonai? I will return to you at the time of birth, when Sarah will have a son."

Sarah: [15]I did not laugh.

Narrator 2: She was afraid. She was answered:

Voice 2: You did so laugh.

Narrator 1: [16]The men got up from there and looked down on Sodom. Abraham walked along with them.

64

Sarah Gets Pregnant

Genesis Rabbah 48.18

Torah: Adonai said to Abraham: Why is Sarah laughing and saying, "Will I really give birth, now that I am old?" (Genesis 18.13)

Narrator: Bar Kappara said:

Bar Kappara: Great is peace. Torah even made a mis-statement in order to protect the peace between Abraham and Sarah. That is why Genesis 18.13 reads:

Torah: Why is Sarah laughing and saying, "Will I really give birth, now that I am old?" (Genesis 18.13)

Bar Kappara: It does not say what Sarah really said in Genesis 18.12:

Sarah: How can my old husband and I have a child?

Bar Kappara: But Torah has God edits that statement for Abraham. It comes out as:

Sarah: Will I really give birth, now that I am old?

Genesis Rabbah 48.19

Torah: Is any miracle too great for Adonai? Genesis 18.14

Narrator: Rabbi Yehudah said in the name of Rabbi Yudan ben Rabbi Shimon:

Rabbi Yehudah: This may be compared to a person who had in his hand two parts of a lock and went to a locksmith and asked him:

Man: Can you repair this?

Narrator: The locksmith said:

Locksmith: I made it to begin with. I certainly can fix it!

Rabbi Yehudah: Likewise God said:

God: I created people to begin with. Of course I can give them back their youth!

1. Why did God change Sarah's words in reporting to Abraham?

_____

_____

2. What lesson does this first midrash teach?

_____

_____

3. When God in the second midrash says, "Of course I can give them back their youth!" what is God saying about Sarah?

_____

_____

_____

Paper-Tear Midrash

Use hand torn paper—no scissors, no pencils, no rulers—only glue—to create an image from this story.

The Sodom Debate

Narrator 1: ¹⁸·¹⁷Adonai said:

God: Should I hide what I am going to do from Abraham, ¹⁸since Abraham is to become a great and numerous nation, and all the nations of the world will be blessed through him? ¹⁹I have become close to him so that he will command his children and his future-family to keep the way of Adonai, to do what is right and just.

Narrator 2: ²⁰Adonai said to Abraham:

God: The shouting from Sodom and Gomorrah is very loud. And their sin is very heavy. ²¹I will go down and I will see if they are really doing as they are shouting.

Narrator 1: ²²The men turned from there and went towards Sodom, while Abraham stayed with Adonai. ²³Abraham came close and said:

Abraham: Will you really sweep away the righteous people with the guilty ones? ²⁴Maybe there are

THE CANAANITE GAZETTE

Imagine that you are a reporter for the Canaanite Gazette. Conduct the following interviews.

1. Ask God: "Why did you tell Abraham about your plans?"

2. Ask Abraham: "How do you think you did in your argument with God? Did you win?"

3. Ask Sarah: "How do you feel about your husband arguing with God and telling God what to do?"

68

---

50 righteous people in the city. Will you still sweep it away? Won't you put up with the city if there are 50 righteous people there? [25]You above all should not do this thing, killing the righteous with the wicked, as if the righteous and the wicked are the same.

Should not the Judge of all the earth do what is just?

God: [26]If I find 50 righteous people inside the city, I will put up with the city.

Abraham: [27]Please...

I dare to speak to my Master—even though I am only dust and ashes. [28]What if there are 5 less than the 50 righteous people?

Will you destroy the whole city because of 5?

Adonai: I will not destroy it if I find 45 there.

Narrator 2: But he continued:

Abraham: [29]Maybe only 40 will be found.

God: I will not do it, because of the 40.

Abraham: [30]Please don't be angry, my Master, if I continue. Maybe only 30 will be found there.

God: I will not do it if I find 30 there.

Abraham: [31]Please, I dare speak to Adonai, maybe only 20 will be found there.

God: I will not destroy it because of the 20.

Abraham: [32]Please don't be angry, my Master, if I continue one more time. Maybe only 10 will be found there.

God: I will not destroy it, because of the 10.

Narrator 1: [33]Adonai left after speaking with Abraham. Abraham returned to his place.

Midrash: Eliezer's Sodom Adventures

Sanhedrin 109b

Narrator: In Sodom there was a rule that one who owned only one ox must take care of all the oxen of the town for one day. It was also a rule that one who owned no oxen must take care of all the oxen of the town for two days. Once, an orphan, the son of a widow, was given the oxen to tend. He went and killed them all. Then he said to the people of Sodom:

Orphan: One who owned an ox may take one hide. One who owned no oxen may take two hides.

Narrator: The people of Sodom asked:

People of Sodom: What does this mean?

Narrator: The orphan said:

Orphan: My rule is just like your rule. Just as one who owns one ox must watch for one day, so one who owns one ox gets to take one hide. Just as one who owns no oxen must watch for two days, so one who owns no oxen gets two hides.

Narrator: In Sodom, if someone had rows of bricks, every person would come and take one, saying:

Person 1: I have taken only one.

Narrator: In Sodom, if someone spread out garlic or onions to dry, every person would come and take one, saying:

Person 2: I have taken only one.

Narrator: There were four judges in Sodom, named Shakrai, Shakurai, Zayyafi, and Mazle Dina. Now if a man assaulted his neighbor's wife and bruised her, they would say to the husband:

Judges: Give her to him, that she may have a baby for you.

Narrator: If one cut off the ear of a neighbor's donkey, they would order:

Judges: Give your neighbor the donkey until it grows an ear again.

Narrator: If one wounded a neighbor they would say to the victim:

Judges: Give him a fee for bleeding you.

Note: Bleeding used to be a medical treatment.

69

Narrator: In Sodom there was a rule that one who crossed over with the ferry had to pay four zuzim, while one who crossed through the water had to pay eight.

Once a certain tailor came there. They said to him:

People of Sodom: Give us four zuzim for the use of the ferry.

Narrator: He protested:

Tailor: But I crossed through the water!

Narrator: They said:

People of Sodom: If that is the case, you must give eight zuzim for passing through the water.

Narrator: He refused to give it, so they attacked him. The tailor went before the judge who ordered:

Judges: Give them a fee for bleeding and eight zuzim for crossing through the water.

Narrator: Now Eliezer, Abraham's servant, happened to be there, and was attacked. When he went before the judges, they said:

Judges: Give them a fee for bleeding you.

Narrator: Eliezer took a stone and struck a judge. The judge asked:

Judges: What is this?

Narrator: Eliezer answered:

Eliezer: Give the fee that you now owe me to the man who attacked me. I'll keep my money.

Narrator: In Sodom they had beds upon which travelers slept. If the guest was too long, they shortened him by cutting off his feet. If the guest was too short, they stretched him out.

Eliezer, Abraham's servant, happened to go there. Said the people of Sodom to him:

People of Sodom: Come and sleep on this bed!

Narrator: He said:

Eliezer: I have vowed since the day of my mother's death not to sleep in a bed.

Narrator: If a poor person happened to come to Sodom, every resident gave him a dinar coin upon which the giver's name was written. But no bread was given him. When the poor man died, each citizen came and took back his dinar. They made this agreement among themselves that those who invite a stranger to a feast shall be stripped of their clothes. Now a banquet was in progress when Eliezer happened to be there. They gave him no bread. Wishing to dine, he went and sat down at the end of them all. Said they to him:

People of Sodom: Who invited you here?

Narrator: He said to the citizen sitting nearest him,

Eliezer: You invited me.

Narrator: The latter said to himself:

Citizen: If they will hear that I invited him, they will strip me of my clothes!

Narrator: So he fled outside. Eliezer did this over and over, until they had all gone. He then consumed the entire feast.

A certain maiden gave some bread to a poor man, hiding it in a pitcher. When this became known, they covered her with honey and placed her on the parapet of the wall. The bees came and consumed her. That is the meaning of Genesis 18.20:

Torah: And the Eternal said, "The shouting from Sodom and Gomorrah is very loud. And their sin is very heavy."

1. What kinds of things did people do to strangers in Sodom?

_____

_____

2. What do all of these things have in common?

_____

_____

3. What was Abraham's "big" mitzvah? How does it compare to what happened in Sodom?

_____

_____

4. What can we learn from Eliezer's example?

_____

_____

5. God destroyed Sodom. Where can we see pieces of Sodom today?

_____

_____

Write Your Own Midrash

Nineveh was also a wicked city. God sends Jonah, the prophet, to Nineveh to tell the people that they have to change. Jonah eventually does his job and the people of Nineveh listen to him, take his words to heart, and repent. Write a midrash about a prophet that God sends to Sodom to tell the people there that they have to change their behavior.

Text 12
Genesis 21.1–21, 25.7

Isaac is Born, Hagar and Ishmael Are Sent Away

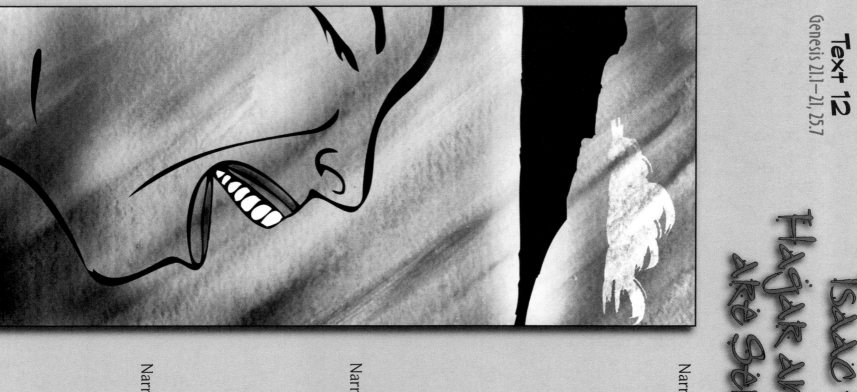

Narrator 1: [2.1]Adonai remembered Sarah as Adonai had said. Adonai did for Sarah as Adonai had spoken. [2]Sarah became pregnant and gave birth to a son. [3]Abraham named his son Isaac (meaning "he laughs"). [4]Abraham circumscribed Isaac his son on the eighth day as God had commanded. [5]Abraham was a son of 100 years when Isaac his son was born to him.

Narrator 2: [6]Sarah said:

Sarah: God has made laughter for me. Everyone who hears will laugh with me. [7]"Who would have told Abraham that Sarah would nurse sons? Well, I have given birth to a son for his old age.

Narrator 1: [8]The boy grew and Abraham gave a party on the day that Isaac began eating solid food.

Narrator 2: [9]But Sarah saw the son of Hagar the Egyptian, whom she had borne to Abraham, mocking her son Isaac. [10]So she said to Abraham:

Sarah: Throw out this slave woman with her son, for the son of this slave woman should not inherit with my son Isaac.

Narrator 1: [11]"This thing about his son (Ishmael) bothered Abraham. [12]But God said to Abraham:

God: Don't let this thing be evil in your eyes because of the boy and because of your slave woman. Whatever Sarah says to you, do as she tells you, for through Isaac shall your future-family be named. [13]But I will make a nation out of the son of the slave woman as well, because he comes from you.

Narrator 2: [14]Abraham got up early in the morning. He took bread and a skin filled with water and gave it to Hagar. He put it on her shoulder, along with the child, and sent her away. [15]She left and wandered in the wilderness of Be'er Sheva. [16]When the water in the skin was gone, she abandoned the boy under one of the bushes. [17]Then she went and sat down across from him—a good way off—about the distance of a bowshot. She said:

Hagar: Don't let me look on the death of the child.

Narrator 2: She sat across from him. The child lifted up his voice and cried.

Narrator 1: [17]God heard the voice of the lad. The angel of God called to Hagar from heaven and said to her:

Angel: What is bothering you, Hagar? Don't be afraid because God has heard the voice of the lad from where he is. [18]Get up, lift up the lad, and hold him tight with your hand. Because I will make him a great nation.

Narrator 1: [19]Then God opened Hagar's eyes. She saw a well of water. She went and filled the skin with water, and gave the lad a drink. [20]God was with the lad. He grew up. He lived in the wilderness and became an expert with the bow. [21]He lived in the wilderness of Paran and his mother took a wife for him from the land of Egypt.

75

THE CANAANITE GAZETTE

Imagine that you are a reporter for the *Canaanite Gazette*. Conduct the following interviews.

1. Ask Sarah: "Why couldn't you tolerate Hagar and Ishmael?"

2. Ask Ishmael: "Was it good or bad to leave Abraham's camp?"

3. Ask Hagar, "How do you feel about the way things worked out?"

4. Ask Isaac: "How was it for you to share your father's funeral with Ishmael?"

Narrator 2: And much later in the Torah we find....

Narrator 1: 25.7 These are the days of the years of Abraham's life—a hundred and seventy-five years. 8 Abraham breathed his last and died in a good old age, an old man and full of years. He was gathered to his people. 9 Isaac and Ishmael his sons buried him in the cave of Machpelah, in the field of Ephron, the son of Zohar the Hittite, east of Mamre, 10 the field that Abraham had bought from the Hittites. There Abraham was buried with Sarah his wife. 11 After the death of Abraham God blessed Isaac, his son. Isaac lived at Beer-la-ḥai-roi.

The Two Wives of Ishmael

Pirke de Rabbi Eliezer 30

Narrator: The wife of Ishmael had four sons and a daughter. They lived in tents in the wilderness. God gave Ishmael flocks, herds, and tents because Abraham was his father.

Later, Abraham said to Sarah, his wife:

Abraham: I am going to see my son Ishmael. I miss him and have not seen him for a long time.

Narrator: Abraham rode one of his camels into the wilderness to find Ishmael. Abraham reached Ishmael's tent about noon. He asked for him but found Ishmael's wife sitting in the tent with her children. Her husband and his mother were not at home. Abraham asked Ishmael's wife:

Abraham: Where has Ishmael gone?

Narrator: She said:

Ishmael's wife: He has gone hunting.

Narrator: Abraham was on his camel. He had promised Sarah that he would not get off. Abraham said to Ishmael's wife:

Abraham: My daughter, please give me a little water to drink. I am tired from the journey.

Narrator: Ishmael's wife answered Abraham:

Ishmael's wife: We have no water and no bread.

Narrator: She sat in the tent and ignored Abraham. She did not even ask him who he was. She was beating her children and she was cursing them. She also cursed her husband Ishmael, speaking evil of him. Abraham heard her words and they angered him. Abraham said to her:

Abraham: When your husband returns home, tell him: "A very old man from the land of the Philistines came looking for you." Tell him that the man said: "When you come home, put away this tent pin that you have placed here, and replace it with another tent pin."

Narrator: When Ishmael returned to the tent, he heard what his wife had to say. He knew that the visitor had been his father, and that his wife had not honored him. Ishmael divorced his wife. Ishmael went to the land of Canaan and he took another wife.

Three years later Abraham said:

Abraham: I will go again to see Ishmael my son, for I have not seen him for a long time.

Narrator: Abraham rode his camel into the wilderness to Ishmael's tent. He asked after Ishmael and his new wife came out of the tent. She said:

New Wife: He is not here, sir. He has gone hunting. Please, stop here in our tent and eat a morsel of bread. You must be tired.

Narrator: Abraham said to her:

Abraham: I cannot stop for I am in a hurry, but you can give me a little water to drink. I am thirsty.

Narrator: The woman hurried and ran into the tent. She brought out water and bread. He ate and drank and he blessed his son Ishmael. He said to Ishmael's new wife:

Abraham: When Ishmael comes home, tell him: "A very old man from the land of the Philistines came looking for you. I brought him bread and water, and he ate and drank, and his heart was merry." He spoke these words to me: "The tent pin that you have is very good. Keep it."

Narrator: Abraham rode off to his home. When Ishmael came to his tent, his wife went to meet him with joy. She told him the words of the old man. Ishmael knew that it was his father, and that his wife had honored him. He thanked God. Ishmael then took his wife and his children and his cattle and all belonging to him, and he journeyed from there, and he went to his father in the land of the Philistines.

Questions

1. What was Abraham's "major" mitzvah?

_____

2. How was he treated as a stranger by his son Ishmael's first wife?

_____

3. What message does Abraham leave for his son? What does the message mean?

_____

4. How was Abraham treated by Ishmael's second wife?

_____

5. What message does he leave for Ishmael? What does it mean?

_____

6. How was Ishmael able to be at the funeral of his father?

_____

The Last Years of Abraham
Genesis Rabbah 60:16

Narrator: Rebekkah first saw Isaac as he was coming from the way of Beer-la-hai-roi, the dwelling place of Hagar, whither he had gone after the death of his mother, for the purpose of reuniting his father with Hagar.

Narrator: After the death of Sarah, Abraham again took Hagar his divorced wife, as it says in Genesis 25.1:

Torah: After the death of Sarah, Abraham again took a wife and her name was Keturah.

Narrator: Why does it say "again"? Because on the first occasion she was his wife and he again took her as his wife.

1. What happened to Abraham after the death of Sarah?

_____

_____

_____

2. Who made this happen?

_____

_____

_____

3. What lesson about families does this midrash teach?

_____

_____

_____

_____

Write Your Own Midrash

Write another letter from Hagar to her father, the Pharaoh of Egypt. Have her tell what has happened to her and Ishmael after they left Abraham's camp. Start your story after the angel appears.

Dear Dad,

_____

_____

_____

_____

_____

_____

_____

_____

_____

_____

_____

_____

_____

Love, Hagar

Text 13
Genesis 22.1–19

The Binding of Isaac

Narrator 1: ²²·¹ After these things, God tested Abraham and said to him:

God: Abraham.

Abraham: *Hineini*

Narrator 2: That means "I am here."

God: ²Please—take your son, your only one, the one you love, Isaac. And take yourself to the land of Moriah and offer him up as a sacrifice on one of the mountains that I will tell you.

Narrator 1: ³Abraham arose early in the morning. He saddled his donkey. He took two servants with him, and his son Isaac. He chopped the wood for the burnt sacrifice. He went to the place which God had told him.

⁴On the third day Abraham looked up and saw the place in the distance. ⁵Abraham said to his servants:

Abraham: Stay here with the donkey. I and the lad—we will go there, we will worship, and we will return to you.

Narrator 2: ⁶Abraham took the wood for the sacrifice and put it on Isaac his son. He took in his hands the fire and the knife. The two of them walked on together. ⁷Isaac spoke to Abraham his father.

Isaac: My father.

Abraham: *Hineini,* my son.

Isaac: Here is the fire and the wood, but where is the lamb for the sacrifice?"

Abraham: ⁸God sees a lamb for the sacrifice, my son.

Narrator 1: The two of them walked on together. ⁹They came to the place of which God spoke. Abraham built an altar. He spread out the wood. He tied up Isaac his son. He placed him on the altar on top of the wood. ¹⁰Abraham sent out his hand to take the knife to kill his son.

¹¹An angel of Adonai called to him from above:

Angel: Abraham

Voice 1: Abraham.

Abraham: *Hineini.*

Narrator 2: ¹²The answer came:

Voice 2: Don't send out your hand to the boy. Don't do anything to him at all, because now I know that you are in awe of God. You didn't hold back your son your only one, from Me.

Narrator 1: ¹³Abraham looked up and saw. Here, behind him, in the bushes, a ram was caught by its horns. Abraham went. He took the ram. He offered it as a sacrifice in place of his son. ¹⁴Abraham called the name of that place:

Abraham: *Adonai Yireh*

Narrator 2: That means Adonai sees. ¹⁵Adonai's angel called to Abraham a second time:

THE CANAANITE GAZETTE

Imagine that you are a reporter for the *Canaanite Gazette*. Conduct the following interviews.

1. Ask God: "What were you testing for? What did Abraham need to do to pass the test?"

2. Ask Abraham: "Why did you go along with God's command? Why didn't you just say 'No'?"

3. Ask Sarah: "What did you think when Abraham and Isaac left the camp?"

4. Ask Isaac: "When did you figure out what was going on? Why did you continue to go along?"

Adonai: [16]I myself promise, Adonai says, because you did this for me and did not hold back your son, your only one, [17]I will bless you by blessing you. I will make you many, very many, as the stars in the sky and as the sand that is on the seashore. Your future-family shall inherit the cities of their enemies. [18]All the nations of the earth shall be blessed through your future-family.

Narrator 1: [19]Abraham returned to his servants. They got up and walked on together to Be'er Sheva. Abraham made camp in Be'er Sheva.

Ram Parts

Pirke de Rabbi Eliezer 31

Narrator: Rabbi Hanina ben Dosa said:

Rabbi Hanina ben Dosa: The ram that was sacrificed instead of Isaac was created just before Shabbat on the first Friday. It was one of the ten miracles that God made just before the first Shabbat began.

Nothing that came from this ram was useless.

The ashes from the sacrifice of this ram became the top of the altar that was in the Temple.

The sinews of this ram became the strings on the harp that David played.

The ram's skin became the belt that Elijah wore. We learn this from 2 Kings 1:8:

Torah: Elijah was a hairy man, with a belt of leather around him.

Rabbi Hanina ben Dosa: The ram's left horn was sounded at Mt. Sinai and at Jericho. We learn this from Joshua 6:5:

Torah: And it will be that when they make a long blast with the ram's horn, and when you hear the sound of the shofar, all the people shall shout with a great shout; and the wall of the city shall fall down flat.

Rabbi Hanina ben Dosa: The ram's right horn, that is the larger of the two, will be sounded in the future, while the exiles are going to be gathered in at the beginning of the World to Come. We learn this from Isaiah 27:13:

Torah: And it shall come to pass in that day, that a great shofar shall be blown. They will come back that were lost in the land of Assyria, and they that were dispersed in the land of Egypt; and they will worship the Eternal on the holy mountain in Jerusalem.

Rabbi Hanina ben Dosa: And also from Zechariah 14:9:

Torah: And the Eternal shall be ruler over all the earth. In that day the Eternal shall be one, and God's name will be one.

Questions

Read this piece of Mishnah.

Ten things were created on the eve of the first Shabbat at twilight and these are they: (a) the mouth of the earth that swallowed Korah and company, (2) the mouth of the well that followed Israel through the wilderness, (3) the mouth of the female donkey that spoke to Balaam, (4) the rainbow that appeared to Noah after the flood, (5) the manna that fed Israel in the wilderness, (6) the staff that Moses used to work miracles, (7) the *shamir*, the special worm that was used to build the Temple, (8) the mystical letters for the Ten Commandments that could be read from both sides, (9) the writing tool that Moses used for his set of the Ten Commandments, and (10) the stone used for the Ten Commandments, and some say also Moses' grave and the ram of Abraham, our Father. (Avot 5.6)

1. What do all the things that God created at the end of creation, just before the first Shabbat, have in common?

_____

2. What makes Abraham's ram the same as the other miracles?

_____

3. What does this midrash teach us about how this ram was a miracle?

_____

4. What is Isaiah telling us will happen "on the day that the great Shofar is blown?"

_____

5. How do all the things that are made out of the ram connect to "that day?"

_____

6. How does the story of the binding of Isaac connect to "that day?"

_____

Angels will Talk

Write a conversation between two angels as they are watching this drama unfold. They know nothing about God's plan and are making their own guesses as to the purpose and result of God's test.

Narrator 1: 23.1Sarah's life was one hundred and twenty-seven years. These were the years of the life of Sarah. 2Sarah died in Kiriyat Arba (that is, Hebron) in the land of Canaan. Abraham went in to mourn for Sarah and to cry for her.

Narrator 2: 3Abraham got up from the face of his dead. He said to the sons of Het (Hittites):

Abraham: 4I am a resident alien among you. Give me property among you for a burying place so that I may bury my dead.

Narrator 2: 5The sons of Het answered Abraham:

Hittites: 6Hear us, sir. You are a mighty prince among us. In the best of our burial-places you can bury your dead. None of us will hold back his burial places from you or keep you from burying your dead.

Narrator 2: 7Abraham rose and bowed to the people of the land, the sons of Het. 8He said to them:

Abraham: If you believe that I should bury my dead out of my sight, hear me. Please be go-betweens for me with Ephron, the son of Zohar, ⁹that he might give me the cave of Machpelah that he owns. For the full price let him give it to me for a burying place.

Narrator 2: ¹⁰Now Ephron was sitting with the sons of Het. Ephron, the Hittite, answered Abraham within earshot of the sons of Het and to all who were in the gates of his city. He said:

Ephron: ¹¹No, sir. Hear me. I give you the field and the cave that is in it. Before the sons of my people I give it to you. Bury your dead.

Narrator 2: ¹²Then Abraham bowed down before the people of the land. ¹³He said to Ephron within earshot of the people of the land:

Abraham: Please hear me out. I will give the price of the field. Take it from me that I may bury my dead there.

Narrator 2: ¹⁴Ephron answered Abraham:

Ephron: ¹⁵Sir, listen to me. A piece of land that is worth four hundred shekels of silver, what is that between you and me? Bury your dead.

Narrator 1: ¹⁶Abraham listened to Ephron. Abraham weighed out for Ephron the silver that he had asked within earshot of the sons of Het, four hundred shekels of silver. ¹⁷So the field of Ephron, that was in Machpelah, that was near Mamre—the field with the cave that was in it and all the trees that were in the field throughout the whole area—was made over ¹⁸to Abraham as a possession...

Narrator 2: ¹⁹After this, Abraham buried Sarah, his wife, in the cave of the field of Machpelah, near Mamre (that is, Hebron), in the land of Canaan. ²⁰The field and the cave that is in it were given over to Abraham as a possession for a burying place by the sons of Het.

Midrash 1: The Death of Sarah

Pirke de Rabbi Eliezer 32

Narrator: When Abraham returned safely from Mount Moriah, Satan was angry. He saw that his attempts to ruin the offering of Abraham had been stopped. What did he do? He went and said to Sarah:

Satan: Have you heard what has happened?

Narrator: She said:

Sarah: No.

Narrator: He said to her:

Satan: Your husband, Abraham, has taken your son Isaac and killed him, offering him as a sacrifice on the altar. Your son cried because he could not be saved.

Narrator: She began to weep and cried aloud three times in sounds that were like the *tekiyah* we sound on the shofar. Then she howled three times in sounds that were like the *tru'ah* we sound on the shofar. Then her soul fled and she died.

Abraham returned home and found her dead. Where did he come from? Straight from Mount Moriah. We learn this because right after the story of the binding of Isaac is Genesis 23.2:

Torah: Sarah died in Kiriyat Arba (that is, Hebron) in the land of Canaan. Abraham went in to mourn for Sarah and to cry for her.

Midrash 2: The Death of Sarah

Tanhuma, Va-Yera 23

Narrator: Just as Abraham stretched out his hand to take the knife, a voice from heaven said to him:

Torah: Don't send out your hand to the boy. (Genesis 22.12)

Narrator: If that had not happened, Isaac would have been killed. At that moment Satan went to Sarah and met her disguised as Isaac. When she saw him she said:

Sarah: My son, what has your father done to you?

Narrator: He answered:

Satan (as Isaac): My father took me and led me over hill after hill, until he took
me to the top of one mountain, built an altar, arranged the
wood, and tied me on top of the altar. He took the knife to
slaughter me. If it had not been that God had told him:

Torah: Don't send out your hand to the boy. (Genesis 22.12)

Satan (as Isaac): I would have been killed.

Narrator: Satan did not make it to the end of the story. Sarah's soul fled
(in the middle) and she died.

Questions

These two midrashim tell different versions of the way that Sarah died?

1. What is similar about these two midrashim?

_____

_____

2. What are the big differences between these two midrashim?

_____

_____

3. Who is Satan? Why does he do what he does?

_____

_____

4. What lesson or value do these midrashim teach?

_____

_____

Sarah was...

Write a eulogy for Sarah. A eulogy is a speech, usually given at a funeral, that remembers the good things about a person's life.

Text 15
Genesis 24.1–27

Rebekkah at the Well

Narrator 1: 24.1 Abraham was old, well along in days. Adonai had blessed Abraham in all things. ²Abraham said to his servant, the oldest of his house, the one in charge of all that he had:

Abraham: Please put your hand under my thigh. ³Swear by Adonai, the God of heaven and of earth, that you will not take a wife for my son from the daughters of the Canaanites whom I live with. ⁴Instead, go to my country and to my family and take a wife for my son Isaac.

Narrator 2: ⁵The servant said to him:

Servant: Maybe the woman will not be willing to follow me to this land; should I then take your son back to the land from which you came?

Abraham: ⁶Do not take my son back there. ⁷Adonai, the God of heaven, who took me from my father's house and from the land of my birth, and who spoke to me and promised me, saying:

God: To your future-family I will give this land.

Abraham: God will send his angel before you, and you will take a wife for my son from there. [8]But if the woman is not willing to follow you, then you will be free from this oath. No matter what, you must not take my son back there.

Narrator 1: [9]The servant put his hand under the thigh of Abraham his master, and swore to him.

[10]The servant took ten camels and some of his master's most precious things. He got up and went to the land of Aram between the two rivers, to the city of Nahor. [11]He made the camels kneel down outside the city by the water well. It was evening, the time when people go out to draw water. [12]He said:

Servant: Adonai, God of my master Abraham. Please, may this be the day that you do the right thing for my master Abraham.

[13]I am standing here by the well and the young women are going out to draw water. [14]Let it be that when I say to a woman, "Please, may I drink from your jar?" one will answer:

Ideal Woman: Drink, and I will also draw water for your camels.

Servant: She will be the one that you have chosen for Isaac. And through this I will know that You have done the right thing for my master.

Narrator 2: [15]Almost before he could finish speaking there came Rebekkah, Abraham's niece. Her jar was on her shoulder. [16]She was very beautiful to look at and had never been with a man. She went down to the well, filled her jar and came up. [17]The servant ran to meet her.

Servant: Please, let me drink a little water from your jar.

Rebekkah: [18]Drink, my master.

Narrator 1: She hurried. She lowered her jar on her arm and she let him drink. [19]When he had finished drinking, she said:

Rebekkah: I will also draw water for your camels until they have finished drinking.

Narrator 2: [20]Hurrying, she emptied her jar into the drinking trough. Again she ran to the well to draw water. She brought enough water for all the camels.

94

Narrator: ²⁶The man bowed his head and worshiped Adonai, and said,

Servant: ²⁷Blessed be Adonai, the God of my master Abraham, who has not forsaken steadfast love and faithfulness toward my master. As for me, Adonai has led me to the house of my master's family.

THE CANAANITE GAZETTE

Imagine that you are a reporter for the *Canaanite Gazette.* Conduct the following interviews.

1. Ask Abraham: "What kind of wife do you want for Isaac?"

2. Ask the servant: "How do you like the job of having to pick the right bride for Isaac? Will it be easy or hard?"

3. Ask Rebekkah: "How do you feel about leaving home, and moving for a husband you have not met?"

Pirke de Rabbi Eliezer, 16

Narrator 1: Rabbi Simeon said:

Rabbi Simeon: The head of Abraham's household was his servant, Eliezer. Where did he come from? When Abraham left Ur, all the local officials gave him gifts. Nimrod took Eliezer, his first born son, and gave him to Abraham as a slave.

When Eliezer came back from this mission to find a bride for Isaac, Abraham set him free. The Holy One also rewarded him.

Tzenah U'Renah

Torah: Please put your hand under my thigh. Genesis 24:3

Narrator 2: Rabbi Beḥaye said:

Rabbi Beḥaye: In those days servants used to put their hands under their masters' feet to acknowledge their masters' rule over them.

Torah: You will not take a wife for my son from the daughters of the Canaanites whom I live with. ⁴Instead, go to my country and to my family and take a wife for my son Isaac. Genesis 24:3-4

Narrator 1: Hizkuni writes:

Hizkuni: Abraham did not want his son to marry a Canaanite woman because the Canaanites could not claim that God wanted them to keep the land of Israel (rather than giving it to Abraham's descendants). Abraham knew that marrying someone from the old country was the only way to keep the land of Israel.

Torah: The servant took ten camels and some of his master's most precious things. (Genesis 24:10)

Narrator 2: Abraham's camels were easily picked out. He put muzzles on them to keep them from grazing in other people's fields. Hizkuni writes:

Hizkuni: Eliezer took ten camels so that they would come with ten riders and he would have a minyan with him so that he could say prayers.

Narrator 1: Laban invited Eliezer into the house and assured him that they had cleared the house of all their idols. Eliezer entered the house. They fed the camels, brought water so that Eliezer and his men could wash their feet, and offered them food.

Eliezer however refused to eat until he had explained that he had come to find a wife for Isaac. Rabbi Behaye wrote:

Rabbi Behaye: The hosts, Betuel, poisoned the food so that Eliezer would die and they could steal his goods. They urged him to eat, but he said that he was Abraham's servant and he needed to wash his hands and say a blessing over bread. That blessing saved his life. An angel turned the platter around so that the portion with the poison food was now in front of Betuel. He ate and died.

Pirke de Rabbi Eliezer, 16

Torah: Isaac brought her to the tent of his mother Sarah. *(Genesis 24.67)*

Narrator: When Sarah was alive, candles burned in her tent from one Friday night to the next. Every week she baked hallah and a cloud with God's presence hovered over the tent. When she died those things disappeared. When Isaac brought Rebekkah into the tent they started over again.

Question

According to the midrash:

1. Who was Eliezer? _____

2. Why did the servant put his hand under Abraham's thigh?

_____

3. Why did Eliezer bring ten camels?

_____

4. What did Betuel plan on doing to Eliezer? Why?

_____

5. What happened when Isaac brought Rebekkah into the tent?

_____

6. Pick one of these stories and explain a lesson or value that can be learned from it. _____

_____

Pantomine

Rebekkah and Isaac meet in the next part of the Torah text (Genesis 24.61-67). Create a pantomime of Rebekkah meeting Isaac. Start with each of them thinking about the other before they meet. Show their feelings throughout.

Text 16
Genesis 25.19–34

Jacob: Round 1—Birth, Round 2—Birthright

Narrator 1: 25.19This is the family history of Isaac, son of Abraham. Abraham fathered Isaac. 20When Isaac was 40 years old he took Rebekkah as his wife. 21Isaac pleaded with Adonai for his wife because she had not given birth to children.

Adonai allowed Isaac's plea to work and Rebekkah became pregnant. 22Twins struggled in her womb and she said:

Rebekkah: If it is like this, why am I living?

Narrator 2: She went to seek out Adonai. 23Adonai said:

God: Two nations are in you. The two families inside you will be separated. One nation shall be stronger than the other. The older will serve the younger.

Narrator 1: 24When it was her time to give birth, twins were in her womb. 25The first came out red. He was hairy like an animal skin, so they called him:

Rebekkah and Isaac: Esau

THE CANAANITE GAZETTE

Imagine that you are a reporter for the *Canaanite Gazette*. Conduct the following interviews.

1. Ask Isaac: "Why did it take you so long to pray for Rebekkah to have a baby?"

2. Ask God: "Why did You give Isaac and Rebekkah twins?"

3. Ask Rebekkah: "Why do you love Jacob more than Esau?"

4. Ask Jacob: "Why was the birthright so important to you that you took advantage of your brother's hungered state?"

5. Ask Esau: "Why did you sell your birthright? Wasn't it important to you?"

Narrator 2: Meaning "the hairy one". [26] After this, his brother came out, his hand holding tightly to Esau's heel. They called him:

Isaac and Rebekkah: Jacob

Narrator 1: Meaning "the heel grabber". [27] The boys grew up. Esau became a man who knew how to hunt, a wanderer in the fields. Jacob was a quiet man, living in tents. [28] Isaac loved Esau because he ate the meat from the hunt. Rebekkah loved Jacob.

[29] Jacob was boiling stew when Esau came from the field. Esau was tired. [30] He said to Jacob:

Esau: Please, let me gulp from the red stuff. That red stuff.

Narrator 2: Because of this, they called his name:

They: Edom (meaning the "red one").

Narrator 1: [31] Jacob said:

Jacob: First, sell me your first-born right.

Esau: [32] I am about to die! What good is the first-born right to me?

Jacob: [33] Swear it to me.

Narrator 2: He swore and sold his first-born right to Jacob. [34] Jacob gave Esau bread and boiled beans. He ate. He drank. He got up. And he walked away. This is how Esau rejected his first-born right.

Midrash 1: Roman Esau

Genesis Rabbah 63.9

Torah: After this, his brother came out, his hand holding tightly to Esau's heel. They called him Jacob (meaning "the heel grabber"). (Genesis 25.26)

Narrator: A Roman official asked a member of the family of Sallu:

Official: Who will enjoy power after Rome?

Narrator: As an answer he brought a blank piece of paper, took a quill and wrote:

Torah: After this, his brother came out, his hand holding tightly to Esau's heel. They called him Jacob (meaning "the heel grabber"). (Genesis 25.26)

Note: In the midrash Esau is often used as a symbol for Rome. He was called "the red one" and Romans wore red armor. Also, the description of Esau as a hunter echoes the image of Rome as a conqueror. Here this verse in the Torah is being used as a prediction that the people of Israel will someday become world leaders in place of Rome. This will be in the time of the Messiah.

Midrash 2: Jacob Versus Esau

Genesis Rabbah 63.10

Torah: The boys grew up. Esau became a man who knew how to hunt, a wanderer in the fields. Jacob was a quiet man, living in tents. (Genesis 25.27)

Narrator: Rabbi Phinehas said that Rabbi Levi taught:

Rabbi Phinehas: Jacob and Esau were like a myrtle and a wild rose bush growing side by side. When they grew up, one smelled beautifully and the other had thorns. For thirteen years both of them went to school and came home from school. After thirteen, Jacob went to the house of study and Esau went to worship idols.

Narrator: Rabbi Eliezer b'rei de Rabbi Simeon said:

Rabbi Eliezer: Parents are responsible for a child until the age of thirteen; but afterwards one must say:

Parents: Blessed be the One Who has now freed me from the responsibility of this child.

Note: This, and not the she-he-ḥiyanu, is the traditional blessing said by parents at a Bar Mitzvah (or Bat Mitzvah).

Narrator: When the twins were thirteen God has Isaac and Rebekkah say this *brakhah*.

Torah: Esau became a man who knew how to hunt. (Genesis 25.27)

Narrator: Esau trapped people with their own words.

Esau: You did not steal? Tell me who was your accomplice. You did not murder? Who was your accessory?

Torah: Jacob was a quiet man, living in tents. (Genesis 25.27)

Narrator: "Tents" meaning at least two tents. Two tents teaches that Jacob studied in two places: in the Yeshiva of Shem and in the Yeshiva of Eber.

Torah: Isaac loved Esau because he ate the meat from the hunt. (Genesis 25.28)

Narrator: Esau saved his best cuts of meat and his best wine for his father's mouth.

Torah: Rebekkah loved Jacob. (Genesis 25.28)

Narrator: The more Rebekkah heard her son's voice, the stronger grew her love for him.

Midrash 3: Jacob was in Mourning
Genesis Rabbah 63.11

Torah: Jacob was boiling stew when Esau came from the field. (Genesis 25.29)

Narrator: Esau asked:

Esau: What is the purpose of this stew?

Narrator: Jacob said:

Jacob: I made it because Abraham has died.

Midrash 4: Evil Esau
Genesis Rabbah 63.12

Torah: Esau came from the field. (Genesis 25.29)

Narrator: Rabbi Phinehas said that Rabbi Levi taught, and the Rabbis said that Rabbi Shimon taught:

Rabbi Phinehas: Abraham lived a hundred and seventy-five years. Isaac lived one hundred and eighty. God withheld these five years from Abraham's life because Esau hurt a betrothed woman and committed murder.

Midrash 5: Esau's Garment
Genesis Rabbah 63.13

Narrator: Nimrod was seeking to slay Esau on account of the garment which had belonged to Adam and which Esau now possessed. For whenever Esau put it on and went out into the field, all the beasts and birds in the world would come and flock around him.

Questions

Midrash 1

1. What are some ways that Rome and Esau are similar?

_____

Midrash 2

2. According to this midrash how were Jacob and Esau different?

_____

3. How is this also a difference between Israel and Rome?

_____

4. According to this midrash why did Rebekkah love Jacob? What does this mean?

_____

Midrash 3

5. What does this midrash teach about Jacob and Esau?

_____

Midrash 4

6. What does this midrash teach us about Esau?

_____

Midrash 5

7. What was the beginning of this story? (Do you remember Adam's snakeskin coat—see page 37?)

_____

Make a Midrash

Write the story of a conflict between Jacob's guardian angel and Esau's guardian angel.

_____

_____

_____

_____

_____

_____

_____

_____

_____

_____

_____

_____

Jacob: Round 3—
The Blessing

Narrator 1: 27.1When Isaac was old and his eyes too weak to see, he called for his older son Esau:

Isaac: My son.

Esau: *Hineini,* I am here.

Isaac: 2I am old and I do not know when I will die. 3Please take your weapons, your arrows, and your bow, and go out into the field and hunt me some meat. 4Make me a tasty treat just like I love and bring it to me and I will eat. Then I can give you my blessing before I die.

Narrator 2: 5Rebekkah overheard what Isaac said to Esau his son. Esau went out to the field to hunt game to bring to his father. 6Rebekkah said to Jacob her son:

Rebekkah: I heard your father speaking to Esau your brother. He said (her version):

7Bring me meat and make me a tasty treat and I will give you Adonai's blessing before I die.

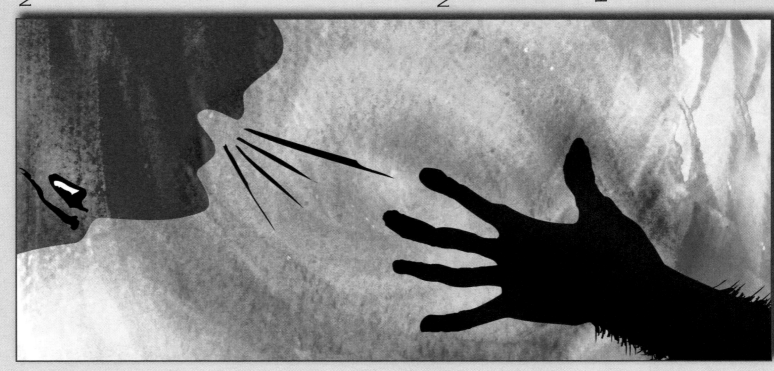

Rebekkah: [8]Now, my son, listen to my voice and do what I command you. [9]Go to the herd and take two good kids (young goats). I will make them into a tasty treat for your father, just like he loves. [10]You will bring it to him. He will eat. And because of this he will bless you before he dies.

Narrator 1: [11]Jacob said to Rebekkah his mother:

Jacob: Esau my brother is a hairy man and I am a smooth man. [12]Maybe my father will feel me, and I will be a trickster in his eyes and bring a curse upon myself, and not a blessing.

Rebekkah: [13]The curse will be on me, my son. So listen to my voice. Go and get them for me.

Narrator 2: [14]He went, he got them, and he brought them to his mother. His mother made a tasty treat, just like his father loved. [15]Rebekkah took her older son Esau's clothes, which were with her at home, and dressed Jacob, her younger son. [16]She clothed his hands and the hairless part of his neck with the goats' skins. [17]She put the tasty treat and the bread she made in her son Jacob's hands. [18]He came to his father and said:

Jacob: My father.

Isaac: *Hineini*, I am here. Which one are you, my son?

Narrator 1: [19]Jacob said to his father,

Jacob: I am Esau your firstborn. I have done what you have told me. Please, sit and eat my game so that you can give me your blessing.

Narrator 2: [20]Isaac said to his son:

Isaac: How is it that you found it so quickly, my son?

Jacob: Adonai your God made it happen for me.

Narrator 1: [21]Isaac said to Jacob:

Isaac: Come close to me and I will feel you, my son, to find out if you are my son Esau or not.

Narrator 2: [22]Jacob came close to Isaac his father. He felt him and said:

Isaac: The voice is the voice of Jacob but the hands are the hands of Esau.

Narrator 1: [23]He didn't know him, because Jacob's hands were hairy like his brother Esau's hands. Isaac blessed Jacob. [24]He said:

Isaac: You are my son Esau?

Jacob: I am.

Isaac: ²⁵Come close to me, I will eat from my son's hunted meat, so that I can give your blessing.

Narrator 2: He came close to him. He ate. He brought him wine. He drank. ²⁶Isaac his father said to him:

Isaac: Please, come close and kiss me my son.

Narrator 1: ²⁷He came close and kissed him, and he smelled the smell of his clothes, and blessed him.

Isaac: See, the smell of my son is like the smell of a field which Adonai has blessed. ²⁸May God give you from the dew of the sky and the richness of the earth and much grain and new wine. ²⁹May nations serve you, and may peoples bow to you. Be master over your brother, and may the sons of your mother bow to you. Let those who curse you be cursed. Let those who bless you be blessed.

Narrator 2: ³⁰As soon as Isaac finished blessing Jacob, Jacob left Isaac his father. Esau his brother came in with the hunted meat. ³¹He had also made tasty food, and brought it to his father. He said to his father:

Esau: Get up, my father, and eat from this hunted meat so that you can give me your blessing.

Narrator 1: ³²Isaac his father said to him:

Isaac: Who are you?

Esau: I am your son, your firstborn, Esau.

Narrator 2: ³³Isaac shivered. He said:

Isaac: Who was it who hunted meat, and brought it to me, and I ate, before you came? I blessed him and he shall stay blessed.

Narrator 1: ³⁴When Esau heard his father's words he shouted a great and bitter shout. He said to his father:

Esau: Bless me, too, my father.

Isaac: ³⁵Your brother came, sneaked in, and took your blessing.

Esau: ³⁶That is why he is named Jacob (meaning "the one who grabs heels"). He has grabbed from me two times. The first time he took my birthright. Here, now, he took my blessing.

THE CANAANITE GAZETTE

Imagine that you are a reporter for the *Canaanite Gazette*. Conduct the following interviews.

1. Ask Rebekkah: "Why did you choose to trick your husband?"

2. Ask Jacob: "Why did you agree to fool your father?"

3. Ask Isaac: "When did you figure out that it was Jacob and not Esau that you were blessing?"

4. Ask Esau: "You were willing to sell your birthright. Why did you care so much about the blessing?"

5. Ask God: "How do you feel about the way things turned out? Who did you want to get the blessing?"

Isaac: [37]I have made him your master. I gave him your brothers for servants. I gave him corn and new wine. What can I do for you, my son?

Narrator 2: [38]Esau said to his father:

Esau: Don't you have one blessing left for me? Father?

Narrator 1: Esau lifted up his voice and cried. Isaac, his father, answered him:

Isaac: [39]You will live in the richness of the land. The dew of the sky will be on it. [40]You will live by the sword and you will serve your brother. But when you fight back, you will break free of him.

The Voice of Jacob

Genesis Rabbah 65.20

Torah: Jacob came close to Isaac his father. He felt him and said: "The voice is the voice of Jacob but the hands are the hands of Esau." (Genesis 27.22)

Narrator: The voice is the voice of a wise man. The hands are the hands of those that skin dead animals!

Another interpretation of:

Torah: The voice is the voice of Jacob but the hands are the hands of Esau. (Genesis 27.22)

Narrator: Jacob has power only with his voice. Esau has power only with his hands.

Rabbi Phinehas gave another interpretation of:

Torah: The voice is the voice of Jacob...

Narrator: When the voice of Jacob shrinks back, then:

Torah: the hands are the hands of Esau.

Narrator: Rabbi Berekiah gave another interpretation of:

Torah: The voice is the voice of Jacob...

Rabbi Berekiah: When Jacob speaks in anger with his voice, the hands of Esau win; when his voice rings out clearly, the hands of Esau lose.

Narrator: Abba ben Kallana said:

Abba ben Kallana: The greatest pagan philosophers in the world were Balaam, the son of Beor, and Abnomos of Gadara. All the pagans gathered before Abnomos and asked him:

Pagans: Do you think we can conquer this people?

Abnomos: Go round to their synagogues and schools. If you find there children with excited and happy voices, you cannot conquer them. If you don't find there children's voices filled with excitement, you can. This is the meaning of:

Torah: The voice is the voice of Jacob...

Abba ben Kallana: When the voice of Jacob rings out in the synagogues, Esau has no hands.

1. Pick one of the interpretations of "the voice is the voice of Jacob but the hands are the hands of Esau." What message does it teach?

_____

_____

_____

_____

_____

_____

2. How is "the voice of Jacob" still heard in synagogues and Torah schools today?

_____

_____

_____

_____

_____

_____

110

Write Your Own Midrash

Write the scene that takes place the first time that Rebekkah and Esau talk after this story.

_____

_____

_____

_____

_____

_____

_____

_____

_____

_____

_____

_____

_____

_____

_____

_____

_____

_____

Jacob's Dream

Note: Jacob's parents send him to Rebekkah's family to find a wife.

Narrator 1: 28.10 Jacob went out from Be'er Sheva and went towards Haran. 11 He came to a place and camped there when the sun had set. He took one of the stones of the place and put it under his head. He laid down in this place. 12 He dreamed. *Hinnei* a ladder was set up on earth. Its top reached the sky. *Hinnei* God's angels were going up and down on it. 13 *Hinnei* God was before him and said:

God: I am Adonai, the God, of Abraham your father and the God of Isaac. The land on which you are lying, I will give it to you and to your future-family. 14 Your future-family will be like the dust of the earth. You will spread out to the sea, and to the East, and to the North, and to the South. All the families of the earth will be blessed through your future-family. 15 *Hinnei* I am with

Imagine that you are a reporter for the *Canaanite Gazette*. Conduct the following interviews.

1. Ask Jacob: "What did you think of when you walked from your father's camp to Beth-El?"

2. Ask God: "What did the dream of the ladder mean?"

3. Ask Jacob: "What did you learn from the dream?"

you. I will keep you in all your goings and I will return you to this soil because I will not leave you until I have done all that I promised you.

Narrator 2: [16] Jacob awoke. He said:

Jacob For sure, God is in this place, and I didn't know it.

Narrator 1: [17] He was awe struck. He said:

Jacob: This place is awesome. This is the house of God. This is the gate to heaven.

Narrator 2: [18] Jacob got up early in the morning. He took the stone from under his head. He set it up as a marker and poured oil on it. [19] He called the name of the place

Jacob: Beth-El

Narrator 1: Meaning "the house of God", though the original name of that city was Luz. [20] Jacob made a promise:

Jacob: If God will be with me and keep me in this journey on which I am going, and if I am given bread to eat and clothes to wear, [21] and if I return in peace to my father's house, then Adonai will be God to me. [22] This stone which I put as a marker will be the house of God. I will tithe ten percent of everything given to me for You.

Dreams Need Interpretation

Genesis Rabbah 68.12

Torah: He dreamed...

Narrator: Rabbi Abbahu said:

Rabbi Abbahu: Dreams have no influence whatsoever.

Narrator: A certain man went to Rabbi Yosi ben H̱alafta and said to him:

Man: I was told in a dream, "Go and bring your father's wealth from Cappadocia."

Rabbi Yosi: Did your father ever visit Cappadocia?

Narrator: On hearing the answer "No", he said:

Rabbi Yosi: Go and count twenty boards in the flooring of your house and you will find the treasure.

Man: There are not twenty boards there.

Rabbi Yosi: Then count from the beginning to the end and back again, and you will find it.

Narrator: He went, did so, and found it. And how did Rabbi Yosi ben H̱alafta figure this out? From the word "Cappadocia," which may be divided into two words in Greek: "twenty" and "boards."

Interpretation 1

Interpretation: Bar Kappara taught: No dream is without its interpretation.

Torah: Here a ladder...

Interpretation: The ladder symbolizes the stairway leading to the top of the altar in the Temple.

Torah: Was set up on earth. (Genesis 28.12)

Interpretation: This is the altar, as it says in Exodus 20.21,

Proof Text: An altar of earth you shall make unto Me.

Torah: Its top reached the sky. (Genesis 28.12)

Interpretation: The odor of the altar sacrifices ascended to heaven.

Torah: Here God's angels...

Interpretation: The High Priests.

Torah: were going up and down on it. (Genesis 28.12)

Interpretation: Ascending and descending the stairway to the top of the altar.

Torah: Here—God was before him. (Genesis 28.13)

Narrator: As it is said:

Proof Text: I saw the Eternal standing beside the altar (Amos 9.1)

Interpretation 2

Narrator: The Rabbis related it to Sinai.

Torah: He dreamed. Here a ladder...

Interpretation: Symbolizes Sinai.

Torah: was set up on earth. (Genesis 28.12)

Narrator: As it says:

Proof Text: And they stood at the bottom part of the mountain... (Exodus 19.17)

Torah: Its top reached the sky (heavens). (Genesis 28.12)

Narrator: As it says:

Proof Text: And the mountain burned with fire to the heart of heaven. (Deuteronomy 4.11)

Torah: Here—God's angels...

Interpretation: Points to Moses and Aaron.

Torah: were going up...

Proof Text: And Moses went up to God... (Exodus 19.3)

Torah: and down on it. (Genesis 28.12)

Proof Text: And Moses went down from the mountain. (Exodus 19.14)

Torah: Here God was before him. (Genesis 28.13)

Narrator: As it says:

Proof Text: And the Eternal came down on Mount Sinai... (Exodus 19.20)

Narrator: Those angels who escort a man in Eretz Yisrael do not escort him outside the land. Thus

Torah: Going up...

Interpretation: Refers to those who had escorted him in the land,

Narrator: While

Torah: and down...

Interpretation: Refers to those who were to escort him outside the land.

Questions

1. What does the story about the treasure teach about dreams?

_____

2. What is a proof text?

_____

3. If Jacob's dream was about the Temple, what was God trying to teach him?

_____

4. If Jacob's dream was about Mt. Sinai, what was God trying to teach him?

_____

5. How do "angels going up" refer to escort angels from Eretz Yisrael?

_____

6. What does this last midrash teach?

_____

Write Your Own Midrash

Write the song the angels sang on the ladder between the rungs.

Two Weddings

Narrator 1: ²⁹·¹Jacob resumed his journey and came to the land of the families of the East. ²He looked, and *hinnei*, a well was in the field, and *hinnei*, there were three flocks of sheep resting by it. From that well the flocks were watered. A great stone covered the well's mouth. ³There all the flocks gathered. The stone was rolled from the well's mouth, and the sheep were watered. Then the stone was put back on the well's mouth in its place. ⁴And Jacob said to them:

Jacob: My brothers, where do you come from?

Shepherds: They said:

Jacob: We come from Ḥaran.

Narrator 2: ⁵He said to them:

Jacob: Do you know Laban, the son of Nahor?

Narrator 1: And they said:

Shepherds: We know him.

Jacob: ⁶Is it well with him?

Shepherds: It is well, and, *hinnei*, here is Rachel, his daughter, coming with the sheep.

Jacob: 7There is still a lot of day left. It is not time to gather the cattle together. Water your sheep and go and feed them.

Shepherds: 8We can't until all the flocks are gathered together. Then all of us roll the stone from the well's mouth. Then we water the sheep.

Narrator 1: 9While he was yet speaking with them, Rachel came with her father's sheep; for she was a shepherdess. 10It came to pass when Jacob saw Rachel, the daughter of Laban, his mother's brother, and the sheep of Laban…Jacob went and rolled the stone from the well's mouth. He watered the flock of Laban, his mother's brother. 11Jacob kissed Rachel, lifted up his voice and cried. 12And Jacob told Rachel that he was her father's relative, that he was Rebekkah's son. She ran and told her father.

Narrator 2: 13It came to pass, when Laban heard the news about Jacob, his sister's son, he ran to meet him. He hugged him, kissed him, and brought him to his house. He told Laban all the news. 14Laban said to him:

Laban: You are my bone and my flesh.

Narrator 1: He stayed with them a month. 15Then Laban said to Jacob:

Laban: Just because you are like a brother to me, why should you serve me for free? Tell me what payment you want.

Narrator 2: 16Laban had two daughters. The older was named Leah. The younger was named Rachel. 17Leah had weak eyes. Rachel was nicely shaped and nice to look at. 18Jacob loved Rachel.

Jacob: I will serve you for seven years for Rachel your younger daughter.

Laban: 19It is better for me to give her to you than to give her to any other man. Live here with me.

Narrator 1: 20Jacob served for Rachel for seven years. In his eyes it was just like a few days because he loved her. 21Jacob said to Laban:

Jacob: Bring me my wife for my days of labor are completed.

Narrator 1: 22Laban gathered all the people of the place. He made a party with wine and food. 23In the evening he took Leah his daughter and brought her to him. 24(Laban gave his woman-servant, Zilpah, to Leah to be her maid.)

25Morning came, and *hinnei*, there was Leah. Jacob said to Laban:

119

THE CANAANITE GAZETTE

Imagine that you are a reporter for the *Canaanite Gazette*. Conduct the following interviews.

1. Ask Jacob: "What did you think when you first saw Rachel?"

2. Ask Leah: "Why did you let your father trick Jacob into marrying you?"

3. Ask Laban: "What did you think of Jacob?"

4. Ask Rachel: "What did it feel like to be the second wife?"

Jacob: What is this you did to me? I served you for Rachel. Why did you trick me?

Laban: [29]"We don't do that in our place. We don't give the younger daughter before the older daughter. [27]Complete the wedding week and I will give the younger to you, too, as payment for service with me. Serve me another seven years.

Narrator: [28]Jacob did this. After the wedding week, Laban gave him Rachel, his daughter, to be his wife. [29] (Laban gave his servant Bilhah to Rachel to be her maid.) [30]Jacob married and loved Rachel more than Leah. He served another seven years...

❧

Laban: Look at this small hill. Look at this marker I planted between you and me. [52]I will not cross this hill toward you. And you will not cross this hill and pass this marker toward me to do harm.

Narrator: [31.51]Laban said to Jacob:

Narrator: [32.1]Laban arose early in the morning, kissed his grandchildren and his daughters, and blessed them. Laban left. He returned home.

Sisters

Lamentations Rabbah, Prologue 24

Narrator: Rachel spoke before the Holy One, and said:

Rachel: Ruler of the Cosmos, you know that Jacob your servant loved me a lot and worked for my father for seven years in order to marry me. When those seven years were completed, and the time came for my marriage, my father planned to substitute my sister for me and have her wed my husband. It was very hard for me, because I knew of the plot and I told it to my husband-to-be. I gave him a sign that he could use to distinguish between me and my sister, so that my father should not be able to make the substitution. But later I changed my mind. I held back my desire and felt for my sister that she should not be shamed. In the evening they substituted my sister for me and I told my sister all the signs that I had worked out with my husband so that he would think that she was Rachel. More than that, I went beneath the bed that he shared with my sister and when he spoke to her she remained silent, and I gave all the answers so that he would not recognize my sister's voice. I did her a kindness, was not jealous of her, and did not expose her to shame.

Questions

1. What does this midrash teach us about Rachel and Leah?

_____

_____

2. What lesson does this story teach?

_____

_____

Make a Midrash

Zilpah was Leah's handmaiden. Bilhah was Rachel's handmaiden. Write a conversation between the two of them about their mistresses' shared husband.

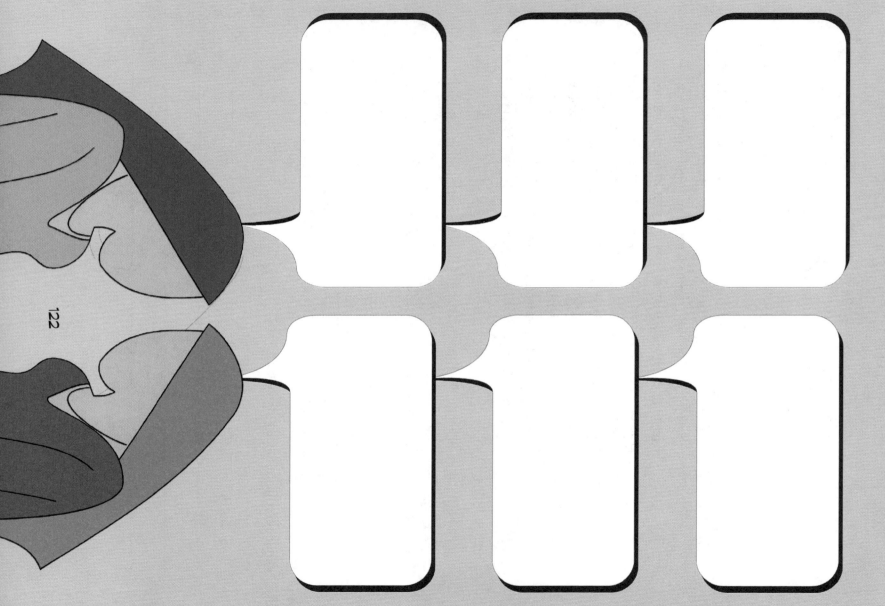

122

The Wrestling Match

Narrator 1: [32.2] Jacob went on his way. God's messenger angels met him. [3] When Jacob saw them, he said:

Jacob: This is God's camp.

Narrator 2: He called the name of the place:

Jacob: Mahana'im

Narrator 1: Meaning "the camps". [4] Jacob sent messengers (angels) before him to Esau his brother. [5] He commanded them, saying:

Jacob: This you shall say to my master, to Esau. "I have lived with Laban, stayed there until now. [6] I have cattle, donkeys, sheep, and servants. I am letting you know this, my master, to find favor in your eyes."

Narrator 2: The messengers returned and said to Jacob:

Messengers: We came to your brother Esau, and he is on his way to meet you. 400 men are with him.

Narrator 1: [8] Jacob was very afraid. He split his people and all that he owned into two camps. [9] He said:

Jacob: If Esau comes to one camp and attacks it, perhaps the other camp will escape.

Narrator 2: [10]"God of my father Abraham and God of my father Isaac, You said to me, "Return to your land to your birthplace and I will do good for you." [11]I do not deserve Your mercy. I crossed the Jordan river, and now my camp is split in two. [12]Please save me from the hand of my brother, from the hand of Esau. I am afraid that he will come and kill me, and the mothers with the children."

Narrator 2: [14]"He camped that night. He selected gifts from what was at hand for his brother Esau. [17]These he put in the hands of his servants. He said to them:

Jacob: Cross before me.... [19]When you see Esau my brother... [18]say, "Your servant Jacob is sending presents to my master. He is behind us."

[21]I will wipe anger from his face by the gift that goes ahead of my face. Later I will see his face, when the gifts have crossed before his face...

Narrator 1: [23]Jacob awoke the same night. He took his two wives and their two servants and his eleven children and crossed them across the Jabbok river. [24]He took them, and crossed them, and had all that was his brought across the river. [25]And Jacob was left alone. And a man wrestled with him until the dawn. [26]When the other saw that he could not win, he touched Jacob's leg and twisted his hip while wrestling with him.

Wrestler: [27]Let me go; the sun is rising.

Jacob: I won't let you go unless you bless me.

Wrestler: [28]What is your name?

Jacob: Jacob

Narrator 2: Meaning "one who grabs heels".

Wrestler: [29]Jacob is not your name anymore. Israel,

Narrator 1: meaning "the one who wrestles with God",

Wrestler: is your name, because you have struggled with God and with people, and you overcame.

Jacob: [30]What is your name?

Wrestler: Why do you ask my name?

Narrator 2: He blessed him there. [31]Jacob called the name of the place:

Jacob: Peniel,

Narrator 1: meaning "the face of God",

Jacob: because I have seen God face to face and my life was saved.

Narrator 2: [32]The sun rose over him as he crossed Peniel. He limped on his foot, because of his hip.

Narrator 1: [33:1]Jacob looked up and saw Esau coming with 400 men. Jacob spread out his children among Leah, Rachel, and the two maids. [2]He put the maids and their children first. Leah and her children were behind them, and Rachel and Joseph were at the back. [3]He crossed before them and bowed to the ground seven times, until he came close to his brother.

[4]Esau ran to meet him. He hugged him. He kissed him and they cried. [5]Esau lifted his eyes and saw the women and the children.

Esau: Who are these people with you?

Jacob: The children with whom Adonai has favored your servant.

Narrator 2: [6]Then the maids and their children came close and bowed. [7]Also Leah and her children came close and bowed. Last, Joseph and Rachel came close and bowed. [8]And he said to him:

Esau: Why did I meet your whole camp?

Jacob: To find favor in my master's eyes.

Esau: [9]I have much my brother. Let what is yours be yours.

Jacob: [10]Please, if I have found favor in your eyes, take this gift from my hand, because when I see your face, it is like seeing the face of God. You have been good to me. [11]Please take this gift of blessing that I brought you, because Adonai has favored me and I have everything.

Narrator 1: He urged him and he took it.

Narrator 2: [12]Esau said:

Esau: Let us travel, and I will go along with you.

125

THE CANAANITE GAZETTE

Imagine that you are a reporter for the *Canaanite Gazette*. Conduct the following interviews.

1. Ask Jacob's wrestling partner: "Who are you and why did you fight Jacob?"

2. Ask Jacob: "What did you think when you saw your brother Esau?"

3. Ask Esau: "Why were you nice to Jacob after all he did to you?"

4. Ask Israel: "What does your new name mean to you?"

Jacob: [13]Know that the children are young, and the sheep and the oxen have newborns. If you drive them hard the flocks will die. [14]My master, please cross ahead of your servant, and I will travel at the speed of the herd and at the speed of the children.

Narrator 1: [16]That day, Esau returned to Seir. [17]Jacob traveled to Sukkot. He built himself a house and made *sukkot* (meaning "booths") for his cattle. That is why the place is called Sukkot.

The Face of God

Genesis Rabbah 77.3

Narrator: Rabbi Hama ben Rabbi Hanina said:

Rabbi Hama: Jacob wrestled with Esau's guardian angel. Jacob hinted at this to Esau when he said to him:

Torah: Because when I see your face, it is like seeing the face of God. You have been good to me. (Genesis 33.10)

Rabbi Hama: This may be compared to an athlete who was wrestling with a royal prince. Lifting up his eyes and seeing the king standing near him, he threw himself down before the King.

Thus it is written:

Torah: When he saw that he could not win. (Gen. 32.26)

Narrator: Rabbi Levi interpreted that to mean:

Rabbi Levi: And Jacob saw the Shehinah (God's presence).

Narrator: Rabbi Berekiah said:

Rabbi Berekiah: We do not know who was victorious, whether the angel or Jacob.

Question

Expand the argument between Rabbi Levi and Rabbi Berekiah.

_____

_____

_____

_____

_____

_____

_____

_____

Write Your Own Midrash

Have the angel who wrestled Jacob tell the story of his match with Jacob to another angel.

Text 21
Selections
Genesis 37.2 – 45.10

The Dreams Come True

Narrator 1: [37.2]This is the family history of Jacob.

1.

Narrator 2: Joseph (meaning "the added one") was 17-years-old. He was a shepherd with his brothers... [3]Joseph made bad reports about them to his father. Israel loved Joseph best of all his sons. He made him a robe of many colors. [4]When his brothers saw that his father loved him more than all his brothers, they hated him and could not speak peacefully to him. [5]Joseph dreamed a dream and he told it to his brothers. This added to their hate. [6]He said to them:

Joseph: Please, hear this dream which I dreamed. [7]We were tying bundles of grain out in the field, when my bundle rose up and your bundles gathered around and bowed to my bundle.

Narrator 1: [8]His brothers said to him:

Brothers: Are you going to be a king, being king to us? Are you going to be a ruler, ruling over us?"

Narrator 2: His dreams and his words added to their hate. [9]He dreamed another dream and told it to his brothers. He said:

Joseph: I dreamed another dream. The sun, the moon, and stars were bowing down to me.

Narrator 1: [10]When he told it to his father and his brothers, his father scolded him:

Israel: What kind of dream is this you dreamed? Am I, your mother, and your brothers, to come and bow down to the ground before you?

2.

Narrator 2: [13]Israel said to Joseph:

Israel: Your brothers are tending the sheep in Shechem. Come, I will send you to them.

Joseph: *Hineini*, I am here.

Israel: [14]Please go and check on your brothers and check on the sheep. Then return and tell me.

Narrator 1: Joseph went after his brothers and found them in Dothan. [18]They saw him coming. Before he could get close, they plotted against him to kill him. [19]The brothers said to each other:

Brothers: Here, the master of dreams is coming. [20]Let us kill him and throw him in a pit, and say a wild animal ate him. Then we'll see if his dreams come true.

Narrator 2: [21]Reuben heard this and tried to save him. He said:

Reuben: Let us not take his life. [22]Spill no blood. Throw him in this pit in the wilderness, but don't lay a hand on him.

Narrator 1: This was so that he could save him from their hands and return him to his father.

[23]When Joseph came to his brothers they stripped off his robe of many colors, grabbed him, [24]and threw him in the pit. [25]Then they sat down to eat bread.

130

They looked up and saw: a caravan of Ishmaelites were coming from Gilead. Their camels were carrying gum, balm, and perfume and they were going down to Egypt. ²⁶Judah said to his brothers:

Judah: What do we get out of killing our brother and hiding his blood? ²⁷Let's sell him to the Ishmaelites and our hands will not murder. He is our brother and of our flesh.

Narrator 2: ²⁸They grabbed Joseph, pulled him up from the pit, and sold him to the Ishmaelites for twenty shekels of silver. They brought Joseph to Egypt. ²⁹Reuben came back to the pit. Joseph was not in the pit. Reuben tore his robe. ³⁰He returned to his brothers and said:

Reuben: The boy is gone. What is going to happen to me?

Narrator 1: ³¹They butchered a goat and dipped Joseph's robe in the blood. ³²They brought the robe of many colors to their father and said:

Brothers: We found this. Do you recognize it? Is this your son's robe?

Narrator 2: ³³He recognized it and said:

Israel: My son's robe! A wild beast has torn Joseph to pieces and eaten him.

Narrator 1: ³⁴Jacob tore his robe and mourned his son...

3.

Narrator 2: ³⁹:¹Joseph was taken down to Egypt. Potiphar, Pharaoh's chief overseer, bought him from the hands of the Ishmaelites. ²Adonai was with Joseph. He was a man who succeeded. He lived in the house of his Egyptian master. ³His master discovered that Adonai was with Joseph when everything placed in Joseph's hands succeeded. ⁴Joseph found favor in his eyes. Joseph personally served him. Everything that was his, he put in Joseph's hands. ¹⁸Adonai blessed this Egyptian's house because of Joseph. ⁶Joseph was nicely shaped and nice to look at. ⁷His master's wife set her eyes on Joseph and said:

Potiphar's Wife: Love me.

Narrator 1: ⁸He refused. He said to his master's wife:

Joseph: My master has put everything in my hands and he doesn't know what is happening in the house. You are his wife. How could I do such a great evil as this and sin against God?

131

Narrator 2: ¹⁰"She would ask Joseph every day, and he paid no attention to her. ¹¹One such day he came into the house to do his work. No one else was at home. ¹²She grabbed his robe, saying:

Potiphar's Wife: Love me.

Narrator 1: ¹³He left his robe in her hand and ran away. ¹⁴She called for the household slaves.

Potiphar's Wife: The Hebrew slave came to touch me. ¹⁵When I raised my voice and screamed, he left his robe and ran away...

4.

Narrator 2: ¹⁹"When his master heard his wife's story, he burned with anger. ²⁰He threw Joseph in the king's dungeon. ²¹Even in the dungeon, Adonai was with Joseph. Joseph found favor in the eyes of the dungeon-master. ²²The dungeon-master put in Joseph's hands all the prisoners and all that was done there. ²³The dungeon-master didn't need to check on anything Joseph did, because Adonai was with him. Everything he did, Adonai made succeed.

Narrator 1: ⁴:¹It happened after these things that the butler of the king of Egypt and his baker angered their master, Pharaoh, the king of Egypt. ²Pharaoh was angry with his two officers, with the chief butler and with the chief baker. ³He put them under guard, under the dungeon-master, in the prison, the place where Joseph was imprisoned. ⁴And the dungeon-master ordered Joseph to be with them. He served them and they continued a long time under guard. ⁵And they both dreamed a dream, each his own dream, that same night. ⁶The next morning they were sad. ⁷Joseph asked them what was wrong. ⁸They told him:

Butler & Baker: We dreamed dreams, and there is no one to tell us what they mean.

Narrator 1: Joseph said to them:

Joseph: Don't meanings come from God? Tell me the dreams.

Butler: ⁹I saw a grapevine ¹⁰with three branches. Before my eyes the buds turned into flowers, and the grapes became ripe. ¹¹I took the grapes and made wine for Pharaoh's cup. Then I gave the cup to Pharaoh.

Joseph: ¹³In three days, Pharaoh will bring you back to be his butler again.

Narrator 2: [14]Joseph said to him:

Joeseph: At the right time, remember me. Please, do what is right by me. Remind Pharaoh about me, and take me out of this dungeon. [15]I was stolen from the land of the Hebrews, and here I am innocent, yet they put me in this pit.

Narrator 1: [16]Next the baker tells his dream:

Baker: I had three baskets of bread on my head. [17]In the top basket were baked goods for Pharaoh. Birds came and ate from the basket.

Joseph: [19]In three days, Pharaoh will have you killed.

Narrator 2: [20]Three days later was Pharaoh's birthday. He had the butler return to his job, and the baker he had killed. The dreams come true, just as Joseph explained. [23]But the butler forgot about Joseph.

5.

Narrator 1: [41:1]Two years later, Pharaoh has a dream. He dreamed about standing by the Nile [2]and seeing seven fat cows came out to graze. [3]Next, seven skinny cows came out and [4]eat the fat cows. Pharaoh woke up.

[5]When he falls back to sleep, he has a second dream. Seven good ears of grain were growing on one stalk. [6]Behind them are seven thin and dry ears of grain. [7]The seven thin ears ate the good ears.

[8]No one can explain Pharaoh's dreams. Not even his magicians and not even his wise men knew what they meant. [9]Then the chief butler spoke to Pharaoh, saying: '

Butler: Today I must mention my faults. [10]Pharaoh was angry with his servants, and put me under guard in the house of the dungeon-master, me and the chief baker. [11]And we dreamed dreams one night, I and he, each one dreaming his own dream. [12]And there was with us a young man, a Hebrew, servant to the dungeon-master, and we told him, and he interpreted our dreams to us. To each one according to his dream did he interpret. [13]And it happened just as he interpreted. I was restored to my office and he (the baker) was hanged.

Narrator 2: [14]Pharaoh sent for Joseph. They hurried him from the pit. His hair was cut. His clothing was changed. He was brought to Pharaoh. [15]Pharaoh said to Joseph:

Pharoah: I have dreamed a dream, and there is no one to tell me what it means. I have heard about you. It is said that you know the meaning of dreams.

Narrator 1: [16]Joseph answered Pharaoh:

Joseph: Not I. God will answer for Pharaoh's peace.

Narrator 2: [25]Joseph said to Pharaoh:

Joseph: Pharaoh's dreams, they are one. God has told Pharaoh what will happen. [26]The seven good cows are seven years. The seven good ears of grain are seven years. They are one dream. [27]The seven skinny cows that followed are seven years. The seven thin ears of grain are seven years of famine. [28]What I have told Pharaoh is what God has shown you will happen. [29]Seven years of plenty are coming to the land of Egypt. [30]And they will be followed by seven years of famine. [32]Pharaoh had two dreams because this thing is true. It came from God, and God will quickly do it. [33]Now, let Pharaoh pick a true and wise person and put him in charge of the land of Egypt. [34]Let Pharaoh appoint managers over the land during the seven years of plenty. [35]Collect all kinds of food from the good years to come and store it and keep it. [36]This food will be for the seven bad years which will come. No one in the land of Egypt will die from the famine.

Narrator 1: [37]The plan was good in Pharaoh's eyes. Pharaoh said:

Pharaoh: [38]How can we find another person like this who has the spirit of God in him?

Narrator 2: [39]Pharaoh said to Joseph:

Pharaoh: Since God made all this known to you, no one could be as true and wise as you. [40]You will be over my house. You will command my people. Only because of my throne will I be greater than you. [41]See, I give you all of the land of Egypt.

Narrator 1: [42]Pharaoh took the signet ring off his hand and put it on Joseph's. He dressed him in robes of fine linen and placed a gold chain around his neck.

Narrator 2: The people of Egypt followed Joseph's plan. [4]They stored food during the seven good years... [54]Then the bad years came.

Meanwhile, Joseph married and had two sons named Manasseh and Ephraim. The years of hunger came.

[56]The famine was everywhere. Joseph opened all the storehouses and gave shares of grain to the Egyptians. There was great hunger in Egypt. [57]From all the earth, people came to Egypt to get food from Joseph. There was great hunger everywhere.

6.

Narrator 1: [42:3]Ten of Joseph's brothers went down to Egypt to get food. [4]But Jacob didn't send Benjamin, saying,

Jacob: Something might happen to harm him.

Narrator 2: [5]The children of Israel were among those who came to Egypt because of the famine in the land of Canaan. [6]Joseph's brothers came and bowed to the ground before him. [7]When Joseph saw his brothers, he recognized them but treated them as strangers. He spoke to them harshly:

Joseph: Where did you come from?

Brothers: From the land of Canaan, to get food.

Narrator 1: [9]Joseph remembered the dream which he dreamed. Joseph said to his brothers:

Joseph: You are spies.

Narrator 2: They denied it. To prove that they were not spies, they told him the story of the whole family.

Brothers: [13]We are twelve sons of one man, but the youngest son is still with his father, and the other one is no more.

Narrator 1: He wanted to test them. He asked them to bring the youngest son down to Egypt. He had them locked up for three days. There the brothers talked.

Brother: [21]This is happening as punishment for what we did to Joseph.

Reuben: [22]I told you not to harm the boy.

Narrator 2: [23]Joseph heard this and could understand them, even though they thought he couldn't speak their language.

Narrator 1: Joseph went and cried. At the end of the three days, Joseph gave them bags of grain, but hid their money in the bags. He sent nine of them back to his father and kept Simeon in Egypt, to make sure that they would return.

Narrator 2: The famine was still bad. Even though they didn't want to go back to Egypt, the brothers had no choice. Judah talked Jacob into letting them take Benjamin back with them. When Joseph saw Benjamin, he invited the brothers to eat dinner with him. They were afraid because of the money that was returned, but Joseph's servant explained:

Servant: [43:23]Be at peace. Don't be afraid. Your God and the God of your fathers gave you a treasure in your sacks.

Narrator 1: First Simeon came in and then Joseph. The brothers bowed to the ground before him a second time. When Joseph met Benjamin he cried, but he hid his tears from his brothers. He washed his face and the food was served.

Narrator 2: Once again he sent the brothers back to Canaan with bags of grain. This time he hid a silver cup in Benjamin's bag. At the border the brothers were stopped, the silver cup discovered, and they were brought back before Joseph. Judah came close to him:

Judah: [44:18]My master, please let your servant speak to you. Don't get angry at your servant, because you are like Pharaoh to him. [30]Now if I come to my father, your servant, and the boy is not with us, he will die. [32]Your servant pledged to my father about the boy. If I do not bring him back, I will have sinned before my father. [33]Now, please let me, your servant, be a slave to you instead of the boy. Let the boy go up with his brothers.

Narrator 1: [45:1]Joseph couldn't control himself. He ordered:

Joseph: Everyone leave me.

Narrator 2: [2]When no one else was there, Joseph made himself known to his brothers. He lifted his voice and cried. Egypt heard him. Pharaoh's house heard him. [3]Joseph said to his brothers:

136

Joseph: I am Joseph. Is my father still alive?

Narrator 1: His brothers were too surprised to answer. Joseph said:

Joseph: ⁴Please come close to me.

Narrator 2: They came close, and he said:

Joseph: I am Joseph your brother, the one you sold into Egypt. ⁵Now, do not be pained. Do not feel guilty that you sold me. God sent me before you to save life. ⁹Hurry, go up to my father and say to him: "God put Joseph your son as master over all Egypt. Come down to me. ¹⁰Settle in the land of Goshen and be near me."

THE CANAANITE GAZETTE

Imagine that you are a reporter for the *Canaanite Gazette*. Conduct the following interviews.

1. Ask Joseph's brothers: "When Joseph was a boy what did you think of him?"

2. Ask Joseph's brothers: "Now that the story is over what do you think of Joseph?"

3. Ask Jacob: "Tell me about Joseph."

4. Ask Potiphar: "Tell me about Joseph."

5. Ask the Jailer: "Tell me about Joseph."

6. Ask Pharaoh: "Tell me about Joseph."

The Reunion

Midrash Lekakh Tov

Narrator: When Joseph returned from the burial of his father in the Cave of Machpelah, he passed the pit where his brothers had once thrown him. He looked into it, and said:

Joseph: Blessed be God who caused a miracle to happen for me here.

Narrator: The brothers thought these words of gratitude that Joseph said as a religious obligation, were actually plans for him to take revenge for the evil they had done him. They feared that now their father was dead, their brother would get even for their deeds. They also saw that since their father was dead, Joseph had given up the habit of having them over for dinner. They interpreted this as a sign of his hatred for them.

In reality, this was due to Joseph's respect for his brothers.

Joseph: So long as my father was alive, he made me sit at the head of the table, though Judah is to be the king, and Reuben is the first born. It was my father's wish, and I went along with it. But now it doesn't look right that I should have the first seat in the family. Yet, being ruler of Egypt, I cannot yield my place to any other.

Narrator: He thought it best, therefore, not to have the company at meals. They, not fathoming his motives, sent Bilhah to him with the dying message of their father. This message demanded that Joseph forgive the sins of his brothers. They had invented the message for the sake of peace. Jacob had said nothing like it. Joseph knew that his brothers had made it up only because they feared that he might do harm to them. He cried so that they should put so little trust in his love. When they appeared and fell down before him, they said:

Brothers: You wanted to make one of us your slave. Now we all are ready to be your servants.

Narrator: He spoke to them gently, and tried to convince them that he harbored no evil design against them. He said:

Joseph: Do not be afraid. I will do you no harm for I fear God. If you think I failed to have you sit at my table because of anger at

138

you, God knows the intentions of my heart. God knows that I acted out of consideration for the respect I owe to you. There is no way that I would lay hands upon those whom both God and my father blessed.

Narrator: From then on, the family regularly had Shabbat dinner at Bilhah's house.

Question

What is the lesson of this midrash?

_____

_____

_____

_____

_____

_____

_____

_____

_____

Paper-Tear Midrash

Tear your version of Jacob's coat of many colors. Just stripes is cheating. Invent a design.